BIBLE PUZZLER

Quizzes based on the New International Version

CYRIL BARNES

Marshall Pickering
An Imprint of HarperCollins*Publishers*

First published in Great Britain in 1992 by Marshall Pickering

Marshall Pickering is an imprint of
HarperCollins*Religious*
Part of HarperCollins*Publishers*
77–85 Fulham Palace Road, London W6 8JB

Photytypeset by Intype, London
Printed and bound in Great Britain
by HarperCollins Manufacturing, Glasgow

A catalogue record for this book
is available from the British Library

ISBN 0 551 02564 6

Contents

ACROSS

1. Where goods are sold at reduced prices
6. Holy Land
10. Shout
11. Sticks for beating
12. Roman numerals for naught, four
13. Attracts pins and needles
14. Spoken
16. Short, twisted sleep
17. Polynesian tree
18. Figs fall into his mouth (Nahum 3)
21. Irish port
23. Ghanaian port
24. Ohio mixed up
25. 'Joshua held out his javelin towards . . .'
26. Not out
27. Over a hundred believers were gathered together when this day came
30. Used money or time

DOWN

1. 'The Lord is my light and my . . .' (Psalm 27)
2. Every
3. 'The' in France
4. 'How shall we . . . if we ignore such a great salvation?' (Hebrews 2)
5. Sluggishness
6. Two
7. Natural
8. Born
9. Pointless bird's home
10. Pigeon's call
15. [God] 'who made the great . . .' (Psalm 136)
19. Give out
20. Hurried
21. Wet piece of bread, a bribe
22. 'Do not . . . to each other' (Colossians 3)
25. Champion
28. Electroplate
29. Saintly street

2 : Bible Dreams

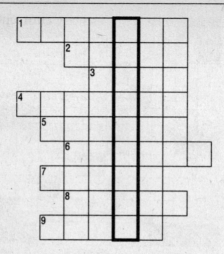

1. He dreamed of cows and corn (Genesis 41)
2. An Aramean who was warned, 'Be careful' (Genesis 31)
3. These men were warned not to return to Herod (Matthew 2)
4. He dreamed in Gibeon (1 Kings 3)
5. He told his dream to his brothers (Genesis 37)
6. His wife suffered in a dream (Matthew 27)
7. A dream comes when there are many (Ecclesiastes 5)
8. He dreamed of a stairway in Bethel (Genesis 28)
9. Usual time for dreams (Job 33)

Central column: A dreaming king of Gerar (Genesis 20)

1. Ol ordo urlo rdho wmaj esti cisy ourn amei nal lthe ear th.

   _____

2. Whoe verco mest omei wil lnev erdri veaw ay.

   _____

3. Li vein pea cewi the acho the r.

   _____

4. Mys hiel disgo dmos thig hwh osa vest heu prig hti nhe art.

   _____

5. Go dlin esswi thcon tent men tisg rea tga in.

   _____

6. Thel or dgiv esst ren gtht ohi spe ople.

   _____

7. Ca stal lyo uran xie tyon hi mbec aus ehec are sfo ryou.

   _____

4 : Same for Three

Add the same word before each in a line to make yet another word; for example: laid, power and run can be preceded by 'over'. All words appear in the NIV.

1. Some, breadth, ful

2. Prints, hills, steps

3. Spring, set, shoots

4. Blood, boat, time

5. Fearing, less, liness

6. Man, dom, will

7. Ager, made, kind

8. Course, falls, carriers

9. Examined, bar, roads

10. Keeper, post, way

11. Grade, born, way

12. Flowing, lasting, more

5 : Eight Bible Gates

The answers to these 'gate' questions appear in alphabetical order.

1. _____ In what cave was David hiding when he sent to the well at the gate of Bethlehem? (2 Samuel 23)

2. _____ Who sat at a town gate and bought some land from Naomi? (Ruth 4)

3. _____ What sort of man was healed at the Beautiful gate in Jerusalem? (Acts 3)

4. _____ What gate did the Lord threaten to break down? (Amos 1)

5. _____ What men sat as judges at the town gate? (Deuteronomy 21)

6. _____ What gates of heaven has God promised to open to pour out a blessing? (Malachi 3)

7. _____ At what gate did the second choir stop in the City of David in Nehemiah's day? (Nehemiah 12)

8. _____ Above which gate did each priest make repairs in front of his own house? (Nehemiah 3)

The words appear forwards, backwards, upwards, downwards or diagonally. Loop each word.

NINE APOSTLES

A.

S	A	M	O	H	T	A	Z
N	C	N	O	M	I	S	P
H	S	A	D	U	J	O	H
O	B	P	Q	R	Y	G	I
J	D	E	C	D	E	O	L
M	A	T	T	H	E	W	I
W	S	E	M	A	J	V	P
H	M	R	I	K	S	N	C

TWELVE NOUNS IN PSALM 1

B.

A	D	E	L	I	G	H	T
T	S	E	A	S	O	N	R
H	T	S	D	N	I	W	E
G	R	R	E	T	A	W	E
I	E	Z	K	M	B	D	S
N	A	M	C	W	B	E	W
K	M	C	I	O	A	L	A
Q	S	N	W	T	P	L	Y

TWELVE HERBS, PLANTS AND VEGETABLES

C.

R	E	B	M	U	C	U	C
M	O	E	Q	E	C	Z	U
A	I	A	M	T	I	P	M
L	E	N	T	I	L	O	M
O	K	A	T	L	R	S	I
E	E	R	I	C	A	Ş	N
K	E	D	A	M	G	Y	B
N	L	M	Y	R	R	H	L

TWELVE TOOLS AND IMPLEMENTS

D.

C	Z	D	R	E	F	W	K
A	H	R	H	S	W	P	N
N	T	I	N	A	I	L	I
P	J	B	S	K	R	O	F
H	A	M	M	E	R	U	E
M	P	X	Q	H	L	G	C
A	W	L	E	V	O	H	S
T	S	I	C	K	L	E	J

7 : Who Are We?

A. My first is in PETER but never in JOHN
    My next's not in DULLNESS but clearly in SHONE
    My third is in EVIL but misses the GOOD
    My next is in CHISEL but not in the WOOD
    My fifth is in EGYPT as well as the NILE
    My sixth's in AMUSE but not in REVILE
    My next's found in JORDAN and in KISHON too
    My last is in ANCIENT as well as in NEW
            My whole's a New Testament letter

B. My first is in WOMAN as well as in MAN
    My next's seen in WALKING, in STANDING and
    RAN
    My third is in TEACHING but never in LEARN
    My fourth's in the STRAIGHT as well as in TURN
    My next's in the HEAVY and also the LIGHT
    My sixth's in the DAYTIME and shines in the NIGHT
    My next is in ABRAM but never in LOT
    My last is in SLEEPER but not in the COT
            My whole took the place of Judas

C. My first is in MATTHEW but missing in LUKE
    My next comes in CHALLENGE but not in REBUKE
    My third's not in LIFE or in TRUTH but in WAY
    My fourth's not in SEEKING but there when we PRAY
    My next is in MALTA but never in ROME
    My sixth comes in LODGINGS although not in HOME
    My next's seen in NEAR and stands clearly in FAR
    My last is in HEAVEN and in Judgment BAR
            My whole is the home of Lydia

D. My first is in BABEL and in BABYLON
    My next's not in COMING but clearly in GONE
    In CAIN lies my third one, in EDEN and NOD
    My fourth comes in JACOB but not in NIMROD
    Both HEAVEN and HAPPY contain my next sign
    While YOURS has no next line but stands out in MINE
    My sixth is in VILLAGE but not in a TOWN
    My last's not in CROSS but shines in the CROWN
    My whole is a son of Jacob

8 : Crossword

ACROSS

2. It is
6. Father of many nations (Genesis 17)
9. In India, once Portuguese
10. King of Judah
11. Unwell
13. Bible sea
16. First Christian martyr
21. By way of
22. Son of Jether (1 Chronicles 7)
24. False prophet named . . . Jesus (Acts 13)
26. Agreeing or going off to sleep
28. Devour

DOWN

1. Goes with Gog
2. Leviathan leaves this in the mud (Job 41)
3. Middle of a clock face
4. Will
5. Stun with wonder
7. Can't say it, even to a goose
8. Conjunction and Roman coin
12. Chinese mile
14. Part of a play
15. First woman
16. Water birds
17. Avoid
18. Greek letter
19. Nun's clothing
20. On Norwegian stamps
23. First half of a street
25. Indefinite article
27. Short for a northern father

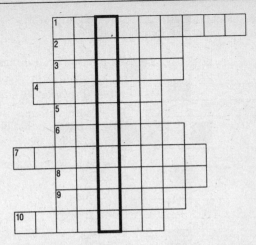

1. They took forty days to prepare Jacob's body (Genesis 50)

2. He cleanses cloth (Mark 9, A.V.)

3. Maker of linen and cloth

4. Israelites were expected to make them without straw

5. He makes bread

6. They worked with carpenters, builders and stonecutters (2 Kings 12)

7. Paul as a tradesman (Acts 18)

8. She grasps it with her fingers (Proverbs 31)

9. Worker in clay

10. A tax-collector (Matthew 10)

Central column: Not one could be found in Israel (1 Samuel 13)

10 : Ten Full Urns

All answers contain the letters URN and appear in
alphabetical order of the initial letter.

1. _____ An offering on the altar
2. _____ Doing this to milk makes
butter (Proverbs 30)
3. _____ Three administrators were
thrown into one that blazed
4. _____ Made by a traveller
5. _____ Tree with bright yellow
flowers
6. _____ To sorrow
7. _____ Done at night
8. _____ '. . . to me with all your
heart' (Joel 2)
9. _____ To repel
10. _____ 'Wise men . . . away anger'
(Proverbs 29)

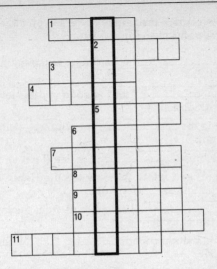

1. Jesus crossed the lake in one
2. Jonah slept below . . . (Jonah 1)
3. Used to row a boat
4. He travelled inside a great fish
5. Made from a cedar from Lebanon (Ezekiel 27)
6. Seaside town near Sidon
7. 'Ships coming from the shores of . . .' (Numbers 24)
8. It is a danger to shipping
9. A centurion unwisely followed his advice (Acts 27)
10. Used to steer a ship (James 3)
11. He built ships at Ezion Geber (1 Kings 9)

Centre column: Paul borrowed a ship from this Mysian city (Acts 27)

12 : Lost Words

A well-known Bible verse will appear as you fill in the
missing words and read them downwards.

1. _____ to the Lord and his strength
   (Psalm 105)

2. For _____ Lord is good and his love endures
   for ever (Psalm 100)

3. Worthy is the _____ who was slain
   (Revelation 5)

4. I am the bread _____ life (John 6)

5. We believe and know that you are the Holy One
   of _____ (John 6)

6. _____ shall separate us from the love of
   Christ? (Romans 8)

7. Blessed is the man who _____ refuge in him
   (Psalm 34)

8. He [the hired hand] abandons the sheep and
   runs _____ (John 10)

9. I am _____ gate of the sheep (John 10)

10. The blood of Jesus, his Son, purifies us from
    all _____ (1 John 1)

11. Jesus _____ Nazareth is passing by (Luke 18)

12. I am the true vine, and my Father is _____
    gardener (John 15)

13. God so loved the _____ that he gave his one
    and only Son (John 3)

1. I SPARE   _____

2. SCRUPY   _____

3. PEGTY   _____

4. GRAY HIP   _____

5. HAPPY MAIL   _____

6. I CON A DAME   _____

7. OH I ATE PI   _____

8. AS RAY IS   _____

9. ERECT   _____

10. PAC A PAID CO _____

14 : Pyramids

Each line needs a letter added to the line above and is then rearranged to form a new word. The last line is made up with letters from the sixth.

A.

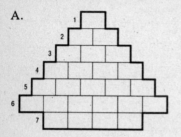

1. Vowel
2. In the same degree
3. Mediterranean is one
4. Brother of Jacob
5. Relish or cheek
6. 'A stone that . . . men to stumble'
7. Tertullus presented his (Acts 24)

B.

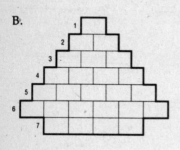

1. Vowel
2. In the direction of
3. Negative
4. Heavy weights
5. Goliath was killed with one
6. Always give this type of answer
7. They were partly of baked clay (Daniel 2)

Add the missing words to complete the following limericks.

A. There was once a poor widow in _____
    Whose son died in terrible pain;
        Then Jesus drew near,
        Said: 'Be of good _____;
    I'll make the young lad live again!'

B. When on the mount _____ met multitudes,
    He never addressed them in platitudes;
        He spoke to them clearly,
        For he loved them all dearly,
    And gave them eight helpful _____

C. With _____ Paul went to _____,
    Where in preaching he was a persister;
        To us it seems odd
        People thought him a god –
    He was just like a brother or sister.

D. Paul wandered through _____ great city
    And thought what he saw such a pity:
        An _____ of stone
        To a god they'd not known;
    Of the true God he told the committee.

16 : Changing Letters

Change one letter at a time to find a connected word.

A.   C   O   R   N

    —   —   —   —   Early part of day

    —   —   —   —   Sound of doves, cattle and owls (e.g. Micah 1)

    —   —   —   —   Lend

    —   —   —   —   Disciples had only one in their boat (Mark 8)

B.   G   A   I   N

    —   —   —   —   Abel's brother

    —   —   —   —   Woman found a lost one (Luke 15)

    —   —   —   —   Sort of cloth

    —   —   —   —   Timothy's grandmother

    —   —   —   —   once 'profit I now consider . . .' (Philippians 3)

C.   C   O   L   D

    —   —   —   —   'Take . . . of eternal life' (1 Timothy 6)

    —   —   —   —   Past tense of above

    —   —   —   —   Not to swear by this (Matthew 5)

    —   —   —   —   Given out by the sun

1. Liv eal ifeo flo veju stasc hri stlo vedu sand gav ehims elf upfo rus.

   _____

2. Thel or dism yst reng than dmys hi eld.

   _____

3. The refo reas weh aveop port uni tyle tus dogo odtoa llpe ople.

   _____

4. B less edi sthem anw homg odcor rects.

   _____

5. B utse ekfir sthi skin gdo man dhi srig teo usn ess.

   _____

6. Thep ray ero far igh teo usma nisp owe rfula ndef fect ive.

   _____

7. T helo rdism ylighta ndm ysa lvat ion.

18 : A Bible Wardrobe

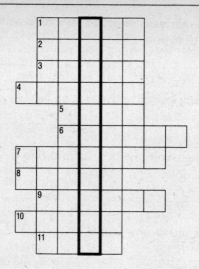

1. General word for clothing and worn with sandals (Ezekiel 16)
2. Gives hair for clothing (Matthew 3)
3. Fragrant with myrrh, aloes and cassia (Psalm 45)
4. Women of Zion wore them as ornaments (Isaiah 3)
5. A wife selects it with flax (Proverbs 31)
6. Women of Zion wore them with their shawls (Isaiah 3)
7. Worn on the Apostles' feet (Mark 6)
8. In Isaiah 3:22, worn with robes and cloaks
9. A rich man dressed in this and lived in luxury (Luke 16)
10. Mordecai wore a robe of this material (Esther 8)
11. More value than clothes (Luke 12)

Central column: A princess wears these garments when led to the king (Psalm 45)

Fill in the blank squares in all lines. Then discover places visited by Paul by writing the numbered letters in the second grid. Two examples are given to help you.

A. The first man
B. Town of confusion
C. The Promised Land
D. Large crowds from here followed Jesus (Matthew 4)
E. Land of corn
F. Governor in Caesarea
G. Threshed wheat in a winepress
H. King of Judea
I. Prophet in days of Ahaz
J. Son of Noah
K. Father of Saul
L. Rose from the dead
M. Paul passed here on way to Troas
N. Ark-builder
O. Land of gold
P. Also called Simon
Q. Desert birds
R. Daughter of Bethuel
S. Good traveller in Luke 10
T. Received two letters from Paul
U. Hittite in David's army
V. Grape garden
W. One lived in Nain
X. King of Persia
Y. Colour
Z. Father of James and John

20 : Add the Figures

In the space provided add the figure to complete the phrase.

1. _____ tribes of Israel

2. _____ God and Father of mankind

3. _____ days and nights of rain in Noah's time

4. _____ Epistles to Timothy

5. _____ Persons in the Godhead

6. _____ Beatitudes

7. _____ smooth stones of David

8. _____ days of creation

9. _____ ungrateful lepers healed by Jesus

10. _____ silver coins given to Judas

11. _____ Gospels

12. _____ Commandments

_____ The total of the figures make the age Jacob claimed to be as he spoke to Pharaoh (Genesis 47)

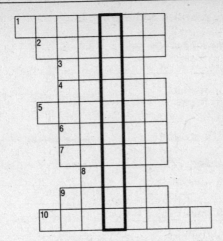

1. What Isaiah said will be there in the desert (Isaiah 35)
2. Brought in by a wind from the sea (Numbers 11)
3. Aaron made it of gold
4. John preached in this desert (Matthew 3)
5. A desert where 'the Lord shakes' (Psalm 29)
6. His men were lost in a desert earthquake (Numbers 16)
7. Israelites' main desert diet
8. This sea divided to help the Israelites
9. He tended Jethro's sheep on 'the far side of the desert' (Exodus 3)
10. First commemorated by the Israelites in the desert

   Central column: Another name for desert

22 : Eleven Lots

Each answer contains the letters LOT.

1. Only one lot for the
   people of Joseph
   (Joshua 17) _____

2. A lot for district
   governor Baana
   (1 Kings 4) _____

3. A lot that ruins the
   memory
   (Deuteronomy 32) _____

4. A lot for dressmakers _____

5. This lot had a sister
   Timna (Genesis 36) _____

6. A lot of ointment _____

7. The behemoth lies under
   this lot (Job 40) _____

8. This lot was a divisional
   leader (1 Chronicles 27) _____

9. A lot steering a ship _____

10. A lot for a schemer _____

11. A keen lot this _____

ACROSS

1. Strike
3. Human being
5. Often goes with drank
7. Engraving is one
   (2 Chronicles 2)
9. Omega (Revelation 21)
10. Every
11. Babylon's was noisy and
    will be silenced
    (Jeremiah 51)

DOWN

1. Son of Noah
2. Number of
   Commandments
4. The sluggard must take
   it as an example
   (Proverbs 6)
5. Girl's name
6. Fish
7. 'Let the wise listen and
   . . . to their learning'
   (Proverbs 1)
8. Metal (Numbers 31)

ACROSS

1. Vessel
3. Abbreviated month
5. If it is dull it needs more
   strength
   (Ecclesiastes 10)
7. '. . . for perfection'
   (2 Corinthians 13)
9. Lived in Sodom
10. Total
11. Before the full grain

DOWN

1. Dove's cry
2. Negative
4. Helmsman
5. Donkey
6. Tree
7. Devoured
8. Spoil

C.

ACROSS

1. Colour
3. Carried by a shepherd
5. Before jamin and hadad
7. Witnessed
9. Tree
10. Conflict
11. Japanese coin

DOWN

1. Coated Moses' basket
2. Land of Cain
4. Number of real gods
5. Goes with arrow
6. Neither
7. The expanse (Genesis 1)
8. Gain victory

A main word fills each strip and can be built up by answering the two or three clues for each puzzle, placing the letters in the numbered squares.

A.

1	2	3	4	5	6	7

Main word (1–7): land known for its cedars. 1, 4, 7, 2: country road; 5, 6, 3: home of Ahimelech the priest (1 Samuel 21).

B.

1	2	3	4	5	6	7	8

Main word (1–8): Sicilian port visited by Paul. 5, 3, 2: 'At midnight the . . . rang out'; 7, 8, 4: the Dead is one; 6, 1: you and me.

C.

1	2	3	4	5	6	7	8	9

Main word (1–9): town on the Sea of Galilee. 3, 2, 1, 4: step; 8, 5: Abraham's birthplace; 9, 7, 6: God's greatest creation.

D.

1	2	3	4	5	6	7	8	9	10

Main word (1–10): Aegean Sea island visited by Paul. 5, 4: preposition; 7, 2, 3: Abraham saw one in a thicket; 9, 6, 8, 1, 10: 'Will you . . . after dry chaff?' (Job 13)

E.

1	2	3	4	5	6	7	8	9	10	11

Main word (1–11): residents of this land visited Jerusalem at Pentecost. 4: round letter; 5, 2, 11: small vegetable; 8, 10, 1: '. . . for perfection' (2 Corinthians 13); 9, 6, 3, 7: majority.

F.

1	2	3	4	5	6	7	8	9	10	11	12

Main word (1–12): One of the seven churches in the Revelation. 2, 12, 3, 8: plague in Egypt; 9, 5, 11, 6: account settled; 10, 7, 4, 1: it comes from the Lord (Psalm 121).

25 : Wells and Springs

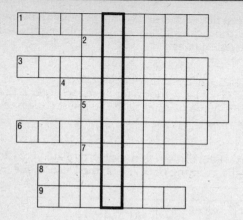

1. Where Isaac's servant dug a well (Genesis 26)
2. Valley made a place of springs (Psalm 84)
3. David longed for water from this well (1 Chronicles 11)
4. God makes springs to pour water into these (Psalm 104)
5. God turned this ground into flowing springs (Psalm 107)
6. This sort of man who gives way to the wicked is like a muddied spring (Proverbs 25)
7. A well associated with Abner (2 Samuel 3)
8. His well was at Sychar (John 4)
9. Who dug the well the Israelites sang about in Beer? (Numbers 21)

Centre column: You will draw water joyfully from these wells (Isaiah 12)

26 : Things in Common

In each line, what have the names or words in common?

A.
1. Tiberias, Dead, Red
2. Omri, Jeroboam, Jehu
3. Nazareth, Capernaum, Nain
4. Lost sheep, lost son, lost coin
5. Livingstone, Xavier, Carey
6. The brothers Dan, Levi, Asher
7. General Booth, Prebendary Carlile, John Wesley
8. Altar, lectern, belfry
9. Romans, Acts, James
10. Philip, Andrew, Peter

B.
1. Shem, Ham, Japheth
2. Gold, incense, myrrh
3. Sardis, Ephesus, Pergamum
4. Canterbury, Salisbury, Ely
5. Asa, Ahaz, Ahaziah
6. Elijah, Elisha, Isaiah
7. Pishon, Gihon, Tigris
8. Zither, lyre, flute
9. Ararat, Olives, Horeb
10. Sun, moon, stars

All words are found in Psalm 46, verses 1 to 7.

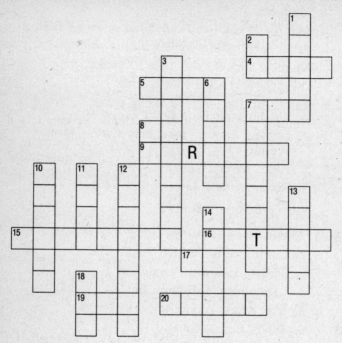

1. The throne of Israel was handed over by David to Solomon.
2. Boaz loved Ruth and called her on to his field.
3. Isaiah enriched the Bible with his writings.
4. We must stick it every time it breaks.
5. The river was filled with rushes.
6. Kirkwall is the largest Orkney town.
7. The traveller called to borrow loaves of bread.
8. To be brave needs courage.
9. Leaving Ullapool the boat sailed off to Stornoway.
10. Jersualem's wall owed its rebuilding to Nehemiah.

29 : Make the Trio

Supply the missing word in each line to complete a well-known trio.

1. Shem, _____, Japheth

2. Gold, incense, _____

3. Morning, _____, night

4. _____, Son, Holy Ghost

5. Latin, Aramaic, _____

6. _____, Meshach, Abednego

7. Ice, snow, _____

8. _____, drink, be merry

9. Faith, hope, _____

10. Way, _____, life

11. _____, tekel, peres (Daniel 5)

30 : The First Psalm

All words are found in Psalm 1.

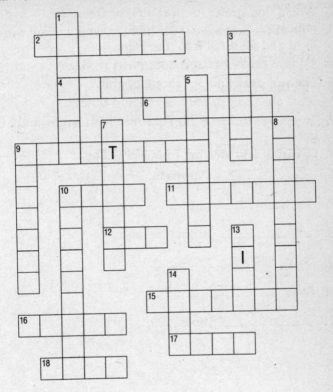

31 : Hidden Bible Rivers

1. It is healthy to eat a banana for breakfast.
2. Would you prefer to meet a raj or Daniel?
3. One of the servants of Elisha borrowed an iron axe-head and let it fall into the water.
4. Samson broke bar and door posts in Gaza.
5. The sun over Philippi shone brightly.
6. Jubal used a cup, harp, a rod and flutes.
7. There was in Kedar no nonsense with lambs and goats.
8. Swearing and stealing I honestly detest.

The answer to each clue is a word containing the letters LOW.

1. They burn away the lead with fire (Jeremiah 6)

   _____

2. Sound of a low wind_____

3. Low ground, but ploughed for use

   _____

4. Low plants with coloured petals (1 Kings 6)

   _____

5. Low land full of milk and honey (Exodus 3)

   _____

6. Low action to become fishers of men (Matthew 4)

   _____

7. Low metal in the fire (Ezekiel 1)_____

8. Low, but holy (Matthew 6)_____

9. Low place for sacrifice (Exodus 27)

   _____

10. Low sound of cattle_____

11. Low, sweet and juicy_____

12. Low soil (Matthew 13)_____

13. Low and scarcely moving_____

14. Low bird (Proverbs 26)_____

33 : Rearrange and Add

Rearrange the letters and add others to complete a word in
the given reference.

1. SALE (Ephesians 5:27) _____

2. SCAR (2 Corinthians 3:10) _____

3. SEAT (Ephesians 6:14) _____

4. SEEN (Philippians 4:5) _____

5. SENT (Acts 2:1) _____

6. SETS (Romans 8:16) _____

7. SHOP (1 Peter 2:1) _____

8. SINE (1 Timothy 1:12) _____

9. SPAN (John 14:18) _____

10. SPIN (Hebrews 12:7) _____

11. STEP (1 Thessalonians
    5:13) _____

12. STUB (Matthew 7:16) _____

All words appear in Psalm 100.

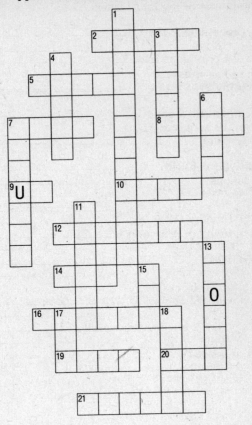

35 : Help in Time of Need

All answers contain the letters AID and appear in
alphabetical order of the initial letters.

1. 'Don't be . . .' said Jesus to
   Simon (Luke 5)   _____

2. Form of hair dress
   (1 Timothy 2)   _____

3. 'The king made a great
   throne . . . with ivory'
   (1 Kings 10)   _____

4. Builder did this with
   foundations   _____

5. Servant   _____

6. Lost, although not for ever _____

7. Settled debt   _____

8. Joab returned from this
   with plunder (2 Samuel 3) _____

9. 'God . . . Let there be light'_____

10. Sober and steady   _____

Complete each name by adding the first three letters.

1. _____ AEL
2. _____ RUS
3. _____ DOD
4. _____ MEL
5. _____ DAN
6. _____ RON
7. _____ TRA
8. _____ DES
9. _____ GAH
10. _____ HAR

11. _____ AUS
12. _____ HOS
13. _____ BIA
14. _____ RNA
15. _____ LAG
16. _____ DIS
17. _____ HAN
18. _____ BOA
19. _____ ENE
20. _____ EAD

37 : Bible People

Complete each name by adding the first three letters.

1. _____ UEL

2. _____ MAS

3. _____ EPH

4. _____ JAM

5. _____ GAI

6. _____ HER

7. _____ HUA

8. _____ ECH

9. _____ ILA

10. _____ ICE

11. _____ SON

12. _____ LIP

13. _____ MER

14. _____ ANI

15. _____ IUS

16. _____ BEN

17. _____ XES

18. _____ SHA

19. _____ DAD

20. _____ ATE

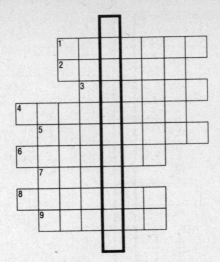

1. Twenty of these was the price of Joseph (Genesis 37)
2. Lydia dealt in this cloth (Acts 16)
3. Some merchants used dishonest ones (Hosea 12)
4. Ships from this place carried heavy cargo (Ezekiel 27)
5. Some turn from their routes (Job 6)
6. Cedar and pine logs were hauled from here to the sea (1 Kings 5)
7. Hiram's ships were filled with this metal
8. Imported from Egypt for 600 shekels (1 Kings 10)
9. Solomon bought them from Egypt (1 Kings 10)

Centre column: Jesus would not allow it to be carried through the temple (Mark 11)

39 : Outspoken Prophets

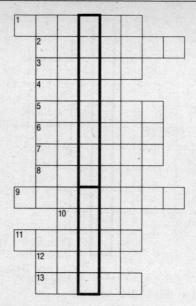

1. Tishbite associated with Mount Carmel
2. Wrote about a valley of dry bones
3. He made a golden calf
4. He met an army as it returned to Samaria (2 Chronicles 28)
5. Once a temple boy
6. Prophet of Shiloh (1 Kings 11)
7. Christian prophet who predicted a famine
8. He wrote an oracle concerning Nineveh
9. He lived in Rehoboam's time (1 Kings 12)
10. He built an ark
11. He told Naaman to wash in Jordan
12. He wrote about locusts
13. Son of Beeri

Centre column: (a) He wrote of a potter at work
(b) He 'refused to be known as the son of Pharaoh's daughter'

40 : Seven-Letter Words

The last letter of the first line is the same as the first of the next line, and so on.

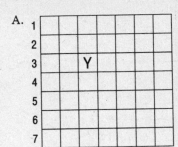

A.

1. A Gospel
2. It will be fair when the sky is red (Matthew 16)
3. Office of a king
4. Produced
5. David prayed: '. . . me from my enemies' (Psalm 59)
6. We must not seek it (Leviticus 19)
7. Father of Azor (Matthew 1)

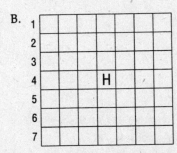

B.

1. 'They began to . . . against the landowner' (Matthew 20)
2. City of Diana or Artemis
3. The wise king of Israel
4. Naught
5. The district to which Joseph withdrew (Matthew 2)
6. Imperial ruler
7. 'And soon the . . . time will come'

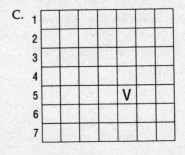

C.

1. He watered the seed (1 Corinthians 3)
2. Sychar was in this district
3. Where the followers of Jesus were first called Christians
4. Godless
5. Jonah was told to go to this great city
6. The reaping time
7. Aramaic word of Jesus (Mark 5)

41 : Metals and Minerals

When all squares are filled in the centre column will reveal
a pattern.

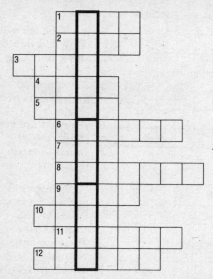

1. This spring cannot produce fresh water (James 3)
2. It is countless on the seashore (Hebrews 11)
3. Mineral for washing (Jeremiah 2)
4. To be worked before repairing the brickwork (Nahum 3)
5. Pharaoh's army 'sank like . . . in the mighty waters' (Exodus 15)
6. Demetrius used it to make shrines to Artemis (Acts 19)
7. Melted with a fiery blast (Ezekiel 22)
8. Used for mortar (Genesis 11)
9. Found in Havilah (Genesis 2)
10. It sharpens itself (Proverbs 27)
11. Smelted from ore (Job 28)
12. Used to make mirrors (Job 37)

ACROSS

1. Son of David
6. Devour
7. Look after
8. Martha and Mary were . . .
11. 'This is the . . . we have heard' (1 John 1)
15. Lines on maps
17. Father of Joshua
18. Between 13 and 19 years old

DOWN

1. They live in Scotland
2. A Yorkshire city
3. A rower
4. Mixed up meats
5. 'My God will meet all your . . .' (Philippians 4)
9. 'Sparkling like . . . and awesome' (Ezekiel 1)
10. An old cloth
11. Damp
12. The people of Shinar used brick instead of this (Genesis 11)
13. A river in Damascus (2 Kings 5)
14. A girl's name
16. May be a currant one

43 : Parents and Children

Each line is the name of a parent or son, and when all squares have been filled the thickened columns will reveal an interesting pattern.

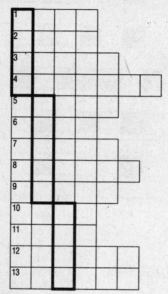

1. Father of Cain
2. Son of Jotham
3. Eighth son of Jacob
4. Son of Joash
5. Son of Isaac
6. Father of Jonathan
7. Son of Jephunneh
8. Hannah's son
9. Son of Jesse
10. Father of Obed
11. Father of Shem
12. Son of Amoz
13. Mother of King Abijah

44 : Twos and Threes

Pair off the syllables to make twelve Bible names or places.
Make the list by the side of the grid.

A.

LTA	LA	LY	JA	JA	ETE
ER	MES	EG	JO	DE	SID
SIL	COB	ON	ITA	AS	BAN
NAH	CR	MA	RBE	YPT	PET

_____
_____
_____
_____
_____
_____
_____
_____
_____
_____
_____

B.

AS	SAM	LOE	ER	TUB	VID
AH	TI	JOA	JUD	OS	JE
OP	DA	SSE	OD	CH	TUS
ASH	AL	MAR	SH	HER	HIR

_____
_____
_____
_____
_____
_____
_____
_____
_____
_____
_____

45 : The Fourth Commandment

All words are found in the Fourth Commandment.

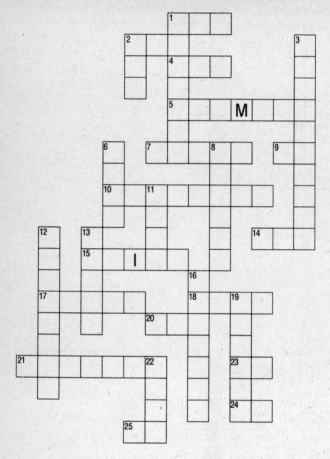

46 : More Names and Places

Fill in the blank squares in all lines. Then discover the names of seven apostles by writing the numbered letters in the second grid. Two examples are given to help you.

A. Wife of Nabal (1 Samuel 25)
B. Once called Luz
C. Paul sailed along its shore
D. Rebekah's nurse (Genesis 35)
E. Elijah's successor
F. Followed Felix as governor of Judea
G. Where Saul died
H. Coupled with Tabor in Psalm 89
I. Son of Abraham
J. Seven when he became king
K. Valley in Jerusalem
L. Lived 777 years
M. Last Old Testament book
N. Remembered for his vineyard
O. King of Bashan
P. Land of Cyrus
Q. Corinthian who sent greetings to Paul
R. Lived in Italy's capital
S. City of refuge in Ephraim
T. Home of Paul
U. Chaldean city
V. Queen of Xerxes
W. Cold season
(E)X. Second Bible book
Y. They jeered at Elisha (2 Kings 2)
Z. Mountain where snow fell (Psalm 68)

49

47 : Harvest Festival

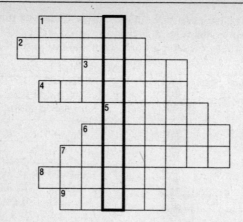

1. 'A certain rich man produced a good . . .' (Luke 12)
2. Tool used by a reaper (Jeremiah 50)
3. With the reaper, who is glad at harvest? (John 4)
4. They can spoil the harvest (Joel 1)
5. Shaken in a sieve (Amos 9)
6. What did God send during wheat harvest? (1 Samuel 12)
7. 'Land that produces thorns and . . . is worthless (Hebrews 6)
8. What a farmer does with seeds to ensure a good harvest
9. What some workmen failed to receive (James 5)

Centre column: What Elisha was doing when God called him to be Elijah's successor (1 Kings 19)

Pair off the syllables to make twelve Bible names or places.
Make the list by the side of the grids.

A.

SAM	ANT	NIAS	SAR	ATH	CAN
EPH	DIS	DOR	SAPP	CAL	ARIA
NAZA	VARY	JOS	AAN	IOCH	SAM
ENS	HIRA	UEL	RETH	ANA	CAS

_____

_____

_____

_____

_____

_____

_____

_____

_____

_____

_____

_____

B.

LYS	ICE	JAH	ARA	TARS	GID
BIA	HANY	TUS	CYP	EUN	DAN
HISH	NAH	JOR	TRA	BET	HAN
RUS	SAL	EON	AMIS	FES	ELI

_____

_____

_____

_____

_____

_____

_____

_____

_____

_____

_____

_____

49 : More Pyramids

Each line needs a letter added to the line above and is then rearranged to form a new word. The last line is made up with letters from the sixth.

A.

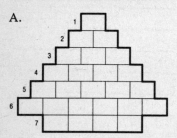

1. Vowel
2. And French
3. Complete collection
4. Sunday is a day of . . .
5. Shed in sorrow
6. Christian festival
7. Followed by the Wise Men

B.

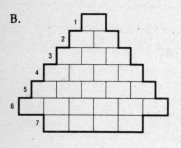

1. Vowel
2. Exists
3. We do this at table to eat and drink
4. Cut
5. Steps in a wall
6. Jesus has many – Son of Man is one
7. Moses was told to make one of their names (Numbers 3)

C.

1. Vowel
2. Abraham's birthplace
3. 'They will . . . and not be weary'
4. What we do with incense
5. Of a town or city
6. Worn on Aaron's head (Exodus 29)
7. My mother's sister

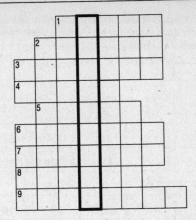

1. Israelites were expected to make bricks without it (Exodus 5)
2. Sister of Moses
3. A store city in Egypt (Exodus 1)
4. One of Egypt's boundaries (Ezekiel 29)
5. Became son of Pharaoh's daughter
6. Eighth plague in Egypt (Exodus 10)
7. King's title in Egypt
8. Sold and taken to Egypt
9. Israel's last meal before escaping from Egypt

Central column: '. . . of Egypt' (Hebrews 11)

51 : Framed Verses

Start with a circled number for each verse. The second
number in each commencing frame will give you the
number of words in the verse you are trying to complete.
The Bible book and chapter is given to help you.

A.

ALL	MY	AND	BE	TO	I	IS
WILL	AFRAID	WHO	MY	NOT	BE	BREAD
SHEPHERD	LOVE	①I 6	AND	ANOTHER	BURDENED	REFUGE
OF	FORTRESS	AND	IS	②COME 16	I	WANT
WILL	ME	⑦HE 7	LORD	IS	④THE 10	YOU
REST	MY	HELPER	WEARY	⑥LOVE 3	AM	LORD
ARE	THE	GIVE	NOT	IS	I	IN
SHALL	③THE 11	ONE	MY	LIFE	⑤GOD 3	YOU

1. John 6   5. 1 John 4
2. Matthew 11   6. John 13
3. Psalm 23 (A.V.)   7. Psalm 91
4. Hebrews 13

B.

YOURSELVES	ARMOUR	YOU	ON	THAT	MORE	WILL
③ IN 14	THAT	ARE	STAND	SCHEMES	THINGS	US
I	WHO	THE	① BE 8	THE	OF	AND
CAN	HE	CONQUERERS	SO	ALL	YOU	THE
THESE	FULL	KNOW	⑤ HONOUR 5	THROUGH	DEVIL'S	LORD
GOD	BEFORE	AGAINST	AND	② HUMBLE 11	FATHER	AM
STILL	UP	WE	④ PUT 18	MOTHER	LIFT	YOUR
THAN	HIM	TAKE	GOD	AND	YOUR	LOVED

1. Psalm 46
2. James 4
3. Romans 8
4. Ephesians 6
5. Ephesians 6

C.

FALSE	THE	SHALL	WAY	THE	FROM	NEIGHBOUR
HIM	AGAINST	LORD'S	MAKE	IN	FOR	LORD
IT	③ PREPARE 11	PERFECT	FOR	① YOU 9	EVEYTHING	ARE
GOD	ABOVE	PATHS	LORD	AND	GIFT	BREATH
WILL	STRAIGHT	THAT	GIVE	PURE	PRAISE	TESTIMONY
THE	YOUR	EARTH	⑥ LET 8	THE	④ THE 9	SEE
IS	② BLESSED 11	GOOD	HAS	FOR	THE	AND
HEART	EVERYTHING	IN	THEY	⑤ EVERY 8	NOT	IS

1. Exodus 20
2. Matthew 5
3. Luke 3
4. Psalm 24
5. James 1
6. Psalm 150

52 : Who Are We Again?

A. My first is in BUTTER and also in BREAD
    My next's not in CUTTING but clearly in SHRED
    I come to the TABLE but I sit not in CHAIR
    My fourth shines in CHERRY but never in PEAR
    My fifth's not in PUDDING though glowing in LAMB
    My sixth's in PINEAPPLE but not in the HAM
    My last is in HONEY, in RYE and in YAM
      My whole is where Jesus dined with Martha and Mary

B. My first is in JUDAS and starts JOHN as well
    My second's in VALLEY and found in the DELL
    My next comes in FORWARD as well as RESTRAINT
    My fourth comes in SINNER as well as the SAINT
    My next is in CITY but never in TOWN
    My sixth sat in tree HEIGHTS but not when it's DOWN
    My last is in HOME, a place of RENOWN
      My whole is where Zacchaeus was chief tax collector

C. My first is in FOUNTAIN though never in WELL
    My next's found in HEAVEN but missing in HELL
    My third's in a ZEBRA and in every ZOO
    My fourth is in NOAH and in his ARK too
    I'm not seen in SYNAGOGUE but heard in the
    PRAYER
    My sixth's in my KNEELING and twice ANYWHERE
    My next's in the SACRAMENT though not in the
    PSALM
    My last's in HOSANNA but not in the PALM
            My whole is where Jesus went to school

D. My first's not in DESERT though where there is GRASS
    My next's not in FIRST TIME but always in LAST
    My third is in LANDING and also in LAKE
    My fourth's not in ERROR but in a MISTAKE
    My next helps in LIFE and in LOVE and in LIGHT
    My sixth's twice in LEFT SIDE but never in RIGHT
    My last comes full three times in ENDLESS DELIGHT
        My whole is a New Testament region and sea

53 : Naaman Visits the Prophet

All answers appear in 2 Kings 5:1–19.

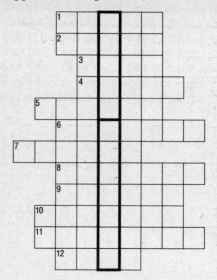

1. Elisha's kind words to Naaman: 'Go in . . .'
2. King of Israel tore his
3. Naaman should do this in Jordan
4. How Naaman left Elisha's messenger
5. Elisha's servant
6. Naaman's illness
7. The man of God
8. Naaman's nationality
9. Israel's river
10. What Naaman did at Elisha's door
11. Naaman would have been had he washed in Jordan
12. A young one served Naaman's wife

Centre column: Two rivers of Damascus

The words appear forwards, backwards, upwards,
downwards and diagonally. Join up the letters of each word.

A	M	O	S	A	M	A	R	I	A	H	O
I	E	P	Y	A	E	A	W	B	C	X	C
C	D	B	L	T	S	D	M	A	R	A	T
Y	I	T	R	U	O	T	F	I	E	D	L
L	A	X	R	N	P	O	N	T	U	S	M
Q	G	P	I	Y	O	H	L	A	K	Y	P
H	Y	A	G	P	T	Y	R	L	M	R	E
C	P	E	M	U	A	C	A	Y	P	I	R
S	B	E	D	O	M	H	M	I	G	A	S
O	D	I	E	U	I	S	S	A	D	I	I
C	J	U	D	E	A	U	C	P	L	N	A
L	N	A	A	N	A	C	R	E	T	E	O

ARAM   CANAAN   COS   CRETE   CUSH
CYPRUS   EDOM   ELAM   EGYPT   ITALY
JUDEA   LIBYA   LYCIA   MALTA   MEDIA
MESOPOTAMIA   NOD   PERSIA   PHRYGIA
PONTUS   SAMARIA   SPAIN   SYRIA

55 : Ten Tents

Each answer contains the letters 'TENT'. Supply the missing word in each line.

1. They speak of you with evil _____
   (Psalm 139)

2. Godliness with _____ is great gain
   (1 Timothy 6)

3. After-school punishment is _____

4. We must pay more careful _____ therefore,
   to what we have heard (Hebrews 2)

5. All your _____ spells (Isaiah 47)

6. To some _____ I believe it (1 Corinthians 11)

7. _____ to instruct one another (Romans 15)

8. A thief at Calvary was a _____

9. Portion to be given to God of mint and garden herbs
   was a _____

10. I have become like a _____ to many
    (Psalm 71)

Add the first three letters to each name.

1. _____ RAH   Where an angel sat under an oak tree

2. _____ RAH   Amos prophesied its destruction

3. _____ RAM   Son of Jericho's rebuilder (1 Kings 16)

4. _____ RAT   Mountain of the ark's resting-place

5. _____ REW   Peter's brother

6. _____ REW   Paul, by race

7. _____ ROD   Mighty hunter

8. _____ RON   Valley in Jerusalem

9. _____ RON   He sold Machpelah to Abraham

10. _____ RON   City of refuge (Joshua 20)

11. _____ RUS   Mediterranean island

12. _____ RUS   Synagogue ruler

57 : Linking Up

A. Join these groups of letters in twos or threes and make twelve New Testament books.

MATT   LU   JO   ES   TI   ANS

REV   MOTH   MA

  DE   TION

RK   HN   Y

PE   PHI   JU   KE

LEMON   TUS

TER   JAM

COLO   ELA   SSI   HEW   TI

B. Join these groups of letters in pairs to name ten altar-builders

NO   ISA   SA   JA   ON

VID   COB   GIDE   AH   AB

RAM   BALA   MUEL   JOS   AM

HUA   MOS   DA   AC   ES

All central column letters are the same.

1. Cousin of Barnabas

2. Mother of John Mark

3. Brother of Miriam

4. Grandson of Obed

5. Grandfather of Joseph

6. Sister of Mary

7. Mother-in-law of Ruth

8. Father of Noah

9. Son of Rachel

10. Grandmother of Ephraim

11. Nephew of Ner (1 Samuel 14)

12. Daughter of Leah

59 : All in the Wardrobe

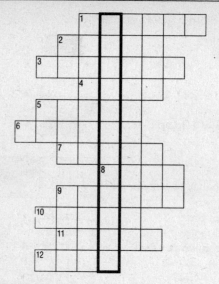

1. Worn by Shadrach and his friends
2. Pharaoh dressed Joseph in fine . . .
3. To be taken off on holy ground
4. Face covering
5. Worn as part of finery (Isaiah 3)
6. Jacob ordered his household: '. . . your clothes' (Genesis 35)
7. Ruth's was filled with barley
8. Best one was put on the prodigal son
9. John the Baptist's clothing was made from this hair
10. Worn in Isaiah's time with fine robes and cloaks
11. Twelve disciples could not take an extra one (Luke 9)
12. Agabus took this from Paul (Acts 21)

Centre column: Worn beneath all others

A.

B.

ACROSS

2. A testament
5. . . . attention or taxes
6. Made by a spider
9. Race of people
13. Self
14. African animal
15. Son of Noah

DOWN

1. God told Moses to go to the . . . of Pisgah
3. Given by Moses
4. Stain
7. . . . nabas
8. Not he
10. Goes with bacon
11. Good in France
12. Ocean

ACROSS

2. Not dry
5. May be listening or deaf
6. Melt in a furnace (Ezekiel 22)
9. Old Testament prophet
13. Not one left in the wall by Nehemiah
14. Used by a fisherman
15. Mineral spring

DOWN

1. To be in debt
3. Devour
4. Prefix for three
7. Cain lived here
8. Thick mist
10. Not allow
11. Monkey or copy
12. Body joint

C.

ACROSS

2. King of Judah
5. To say we agree
6. Old English for your
9. 'Be . . . and repent'
   (Revelation 3)
13. Some
14. . . . lepers or talents
15. . . . in the grave he lay

DOWN

1. Dry grass
3. To plant
4. Tree
7. Japanese coin
8. Small vegetable
10. Busy insect
11. Cereal
12. A pair

Two words are filled in to help you. All words can be found in Psalm 23.

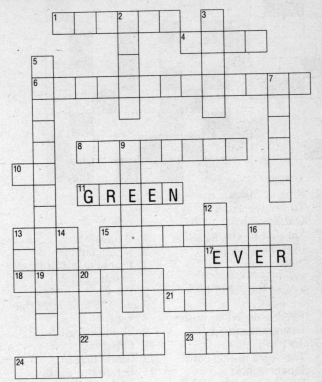

62 : Crossword on Horeb

Clues are based mainly on 1 Kings 19:8–18.

ACROSS

1. Rejected by the Israelites
6. Hazael's kingdom
8. Greek letter
10. Morning
11. Second half of Elijah's successor
13. Ruled from Westminster
14. It was still and small (AV)
16. 'The word of the Lord came . . . him'
17. Before
20. Strength of the wind

DOWN

2. 'I have been . . . jealous'
3. Jehu's father
4. Prophets left in Israel besides Elijah
5. See 7
7 and 5. Came after the wind
9. Thou in French
11. Offspring
12. Brave airman
15. Before the gentle whisper, but in reverse
18. '. . . back the way you came
19. You in Old English

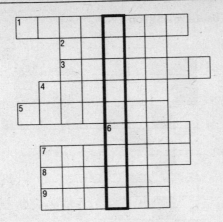

1. Where Ahaz 'saw an altar' (2 Kings 16)

2. Who was Abraham going to offer on an altar?

3. They burned this on altars of brick (Isaiah 65)

4. Where Gideon built an altar (Judges 6)

5. Asa removed these altars (2 Chronicles 14)

6. It burned up Elijah's sacrifice (1 Kings 18)

7. With the Reubenites they built an altar called 'A Witness Between Us that the Lord is God' (Joshua 22)

8. Moses built an altar of . . . wood

9. Where Paul found an altar 'to an unknown god' (Acts 17)

Centre column: Offered on an altar

64 : Collective Nouns

Add the missing words and verse numbers.

1. Band of _____ 1 Kings 11 _____

2. Brood of _____ Matthew 3 _____

3. Bunch of _____ Exodus 12 _____

4. Cluster of _____ Numbers 13 _____

5. Drove of _____ Exodus 12 _____

6. Detachment of _____ John 18 _____

7. Flock of _____ Matthew 26 _____

8. Heap of _____ Jeremiah 51 _____

9. Herd of _____ Mark 5 _____

10. Host of _____ Luke 2 _____

11. Pile of _____ Ezra 6 _____

12. Swarm of _____ Jeremiah 51 _____

In each case find the verse in the given chapter and write the correct words on a piece of paper.

1. The way I am and the life and the truth (John 14)
2. I am the gardener, and my Father is the true vine (John 15)
3. He binds up the broken-hearted and he heals their wounds (Psalm 147)
4. You will find me and seek me when you find me with all your heart (Jeremiah 29)
5. Love yourself as your neighbour (Romans 13)
6. Lift up yourselves, therefore, under God's mighty hand, that he may humble you in due time (1 Peter 5)
7. Love must be sincere. Cling to what is evil; hate what is good (Romans 12)
8. Store up for yourselves moth and rust in heaven, where treasures do not destroy (Matthew 6)
9. As I will be with Moses, so I was with you (Joshua 1)
10. You will keep steadfast him whose mind is in perfect peace (Isaiah 26)
11. Live in harmony . . . as brothers; be sympathetic, love one another (1 Peter 3)
12. Love does not delight with the truth but rejoices in evil (1 Corinthians 13)

66 : Four Directions

The larger strips are linked by three-letter words.

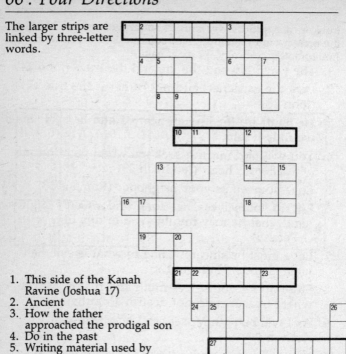

1. This side of the Kanah Ravine (Joshua 17)
2. Ancient
3. How the father approached the prodigal son
4. Do in the past
5. Writing material used by Jeremiah and John
6. Where Cain lived after Eden
7. Not bright
8. It unlocks
9. 'Abraham set apart seven . . . lambs (Genesis 21)
10. Gilgal was on this border of Jericho (Joshua 4)
11. Demand
12. The Revelation is at this part of the Bible
13. (across). Built by Noah
13. (down). Ear piercer (Exodus 21)
14. Son of Jacob
15. Fresh
16. Every
17. Measure of oil (Leviticus 14)
18. . . . in the grave he lay
19. Tribe of Israel
20. 'I will be like the . . . to Israel' (Hosea 14)
21. Foothills subdued by Joshua (Joshua 10)
22. With Samuel in the temple
23. Colour
24. Frozen water
25. Mediterranean island (Acts 21)
26. 'Towards the goal to . . . the prize' (Philippians 3)
27. This boundary started from the Salt Sea (Numbers 34)

67 : Squares of Nine

Look for a starting letter in each small square; then build up a word or name, moving to an adjacent letter each time, horizontally, vertically, or diagonally.

A.

	1			2			3	
E	U	S	Y	O	M	M	U	S
A	A	C	N	T	I	E	N	I
H	C	Z	E	S	T	D	O	C
S	R	A	S	L	P	B	B	E
A	M	I	E	S	I	E	U	Z
N	A	T	D	I	C	B	E	L
E	M	E	H	Z	P	H	P	S
N	N	A	A	E	H	E	E	N
T	T	O	I	N	A	S	I	A
	6			7			8	

(4 at left of second row, 5 at right of second row)

B.

	9			10			11	
H	T	E	T	A	L	P	I	E
L	B	E	I	A	V	T	A	N
E	H	M	S	O	N	S	E	L
S	E	C	O	P	S	A	A	I
I	A	D	T	L	I	M	C	N
L	O	P	E	M	A	E	D	O
R	U	J	R	E	P	I	L	Y
S	E	E	N	A	C	U	L	R
A	L	M	A	U	M	M	C	I
	14			15			16	

(12 at left of second row, 13 at right of second row)

1. Tax-collector
2. Witness
3. Night visitor
4. Kind traveller
5. Prince of demons
6. Made at Calvary
7. Prophet
8. Epistle

Centre: Followers

9. Birthplace of Jesus
10. Seen by Simeon's eyes (Luke 2)
11. Earlier name of Israel
12. District of ten Greek cities
13. Visited by Paul after a night vision
14. Capital of Judah
15. Where Jesus healed Peter's mother-in-law
16. Paul preached the gospel from 'Jerusalem all the way around to . . .' (Romans 15)

Centre: Visited by Paul between Tyre and Caesarea

73

68 : Men and Women of the Bible

A. MEN

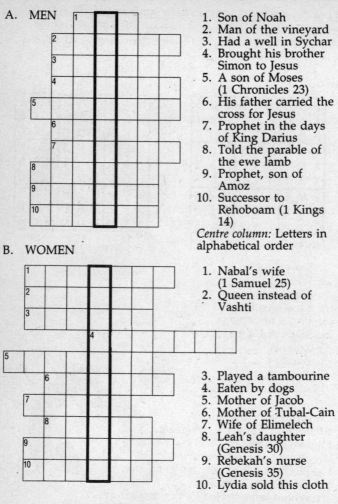

1. Son of Noah
2. Man of the vineyard
3. Had a well in Sychar
4. Brought his brother Simon to Jesus
5. A son of Moses (1 Chronicles 23)
6. His father carried the cross for Jesus
7. Prophet in the days of King Darius
8. Told the parable of the ewe lamb
9. Prophet, son of Amoz
10. Successor to Rehoboam (1 Kings 14)

Centre column: Letters in alphabetical order

B. WOMEN

1. Nabal's wife (1 Samuel 25)
2. Queen instead of Vashti
3. Played a tambourine
4. Eaten by dogs
5. Mother of Jacob
6. Mother of Tubal-Cain
7. Wife of Elimelech
8. Leah's daughter (Genesis 30)
9. Rebekah's nurse (Genesis 35)
10. Lydia sold this cloth

Centre column: Letters in alphabetical order

69 : Wheels of Knowledge

Fill in the spaces according to the clues. The last letter or letters of answer No. 1 are the same as the first letter or letters of answer No. 2, and so on. Each new word starts a new circle.

A.

1. Its walls fell down
2. Old Testament book
3. Seven in the Revelation (chapter 5)
4. Jewish priest with seven sons (Acts 19)
5. A testimony must be
6. False god
7. Jerusalem mountain

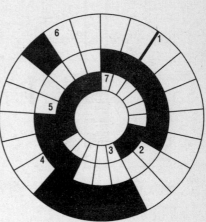

B.

1. Paul arrived here after leaving Rhegium (Acts 28)
2. David said they had fallen for him in pleasant places (Psalm 16)
3. Homes of birds
4. Imprisoned with Paul in Philippi
5. Associated with repentance and sackcloth (Matthew 11)
6. Twin brother of Jacob
7. Time of rain according to Joel (chapter 2)

70 : Flags of Bible Lands

Add the missing consonants.

1. Red and white
. U . . E . (Asia Minor)
. E . A . O .
. A . . A

2. Red, white and black
I . A .   (Babylon)
E . Y . .
. Y . I A

3. Red, white, black and
green
. O . . A .

4. Red, white and green
I . A .   (Persia)
I . A . .

5. Red, yellow and green
E . . IO . IA

6. Blue and white
. . EE . E
I . . AE .

7. White and yellow
. Y . . US

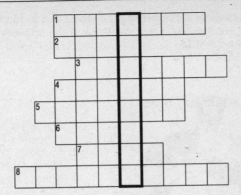

1. Who enter through windows? (Joel 2)
2. What king saw Jezebel sitting at a window in Jezreel? (2 Kings 9)
3. I looked through this at the window (Proverbs 7)
4. What did Daniel do 'where the windows opened towards Jerusalem'? (Daniel 6)
5. Where a scarlet cord was tied in a window (Joshua 2)
6. He opened a window to let out a raven
7. Who was lowered from a window in Damascus?
8. Solomon made these narrow windows in the temple (1 Kings 6)

Centre column: He fell from a window in Troas (Acts 20)

72 : Round We Go

Fill in the spaces according to the clues. The last letter or letters of answer No. 1 are the same as the first letter or letters of answer No. 2, and so on. Each new word starts a new circle.

A.

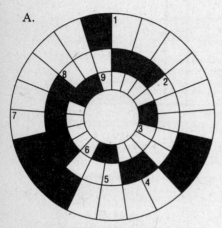

1. Son of Jacob and husband of Mary
2. Measure, ten omers (Exodus 16)
3. King of Israel
4. Cain's brother
5. Priest in Shiloh
6. Rome is its capital
7. Where Peter healed Aeneas (Acts 9)
8. Tribe of Israel
9. Ruth's mother-in-law

B.

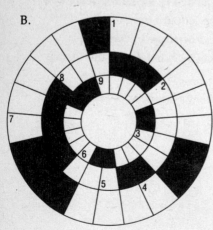

1. River of Christ's baptism
2. 'A time to mourn and a time to . . .' (Ecclesiastes 3)
3. Room in a prison
4. Starts many a Welsh town
5. Industrious insect
6. 'He [Jehoiakim] . . . the land and exacted the silver' (2 Kings 23)
7. Boy's name
8. Writing material
9. We should do this when we pray

C.

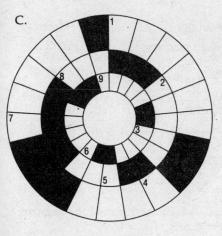

1. Queen of Persia
2. King when Jesus was born
3. Father of Azariah, a prophet of Asa's reign
4. Boundary line or ridge
5. Precious stone
6. Island in the Mediterranean
7. Here Jesus reclined with the Twelve at the Last Supper
8. Choice piece of meat (Ezekiel 24)
9. Fruit from the Valley of Eshcol (Numbers 13)

73 : Twenty Broken Verses

Fill in the missing words and the answers will come in alphabetical order.

1. Break down their _____ (Exodus 34)

2. Jesus took _____ gave thanks and broke it (Matthew 26)

3. The people have broken my _____ (Hosea 8)

4. Starting a quarrel is like breaching a _____ (Proverbs 17)

5. The _____ is broken up (Isaiah 24)

6. How could you break _____ with the God of Israel like this? (Joshua 22)

7. I will break down _____ of bronze (Isaiah 45)

8. A broken and contrite _____ O God, you will not despise (Psalm 51)

9. Can a man break _____ from the north or bronze? (Jeremiah 15)

10. She broke the _____ and poured the perfume on his head (Mark 14)

11. It is time for you to act, O Lord, your _____ is being broken (Psalm 119)

12. You will break to pieces many _____ (Micah 4)

13. Do not break your _____ you have made to the Lord (Matthew 5)

14. I have become like broken _____ (Psalm 31)

15. The Lord has broken the _____ of the wicked (Isaiah 14)

16. The _____ cannot be broken (John 10)

17. I will write on them the words that were on the first _____ which you broke (Exodus 34)

18. Break up your _____ ground (Jeremiah 4)

19. The _____ of Jerusalem is broken down (Nehemiah 1)

20. I will break the _____ off their necks (Jeremiah 30)

74 : Catching Fish

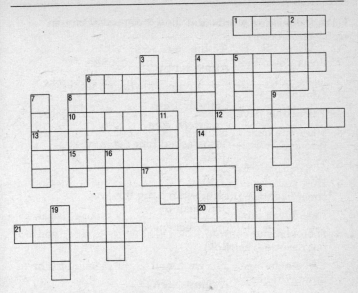

1. Time of Simon's fishing (Luke 5)
2. Fishing tackle (Amos 4)
3. Thrown into the lake by Peter (Matthew 17)
4 (across). Wrote about fishing in 1 Kings 4
4 (down). Place for fishing
5. Another fishing place
6. Bible sea
7. A fish caught him
8. Result of fishing
9. 'Put out into . . . water' (Luke 5)
10. Brother of fisherman Peter
11. Natural habitat of fish
12. Galilean fisherman
13. Fishing mesh
14. Fishing pole (Job 41)
15. Found in a fish's mouth
16. Land of fishermen
17. Fisherman who jumped into the water (John 21)
18. 'I will make you fishers of . . .'
19. Sailing vessel for fishermen
20. Where fish died (Exodus 7)
21. After the resurrection Jesus took 'a piece of . . . fish'

75 : Changing Letters

Change one letter at a time to find a connected word.

A. M O R E   A plus sign
   — — — —   Apple centre
   — — — —   '. . . to me, all who are weary'
   — — — —   Cathedral top
   — — — —   American coin
   — — — —   'Jesus asked him the third . . .'
                      (John 21)
   — — — —   Fruit
   — — — —   Hands can hang this way
                      (Jeremiah 6)
   — — — —   Imperfect speech
   — — — —   Rota
   — — — —   . . . we forget
   — — — —   A minus sign

B. G I V E   '. . . and it will be given to you'
                      (Luke 6:38)
   — — — —   'You . . . me something to drink'
   — — — —   Talk wildly
   — — — —   Speed
   — — — —   A male animal entered the ark
                      with its . . .
   — — — —   Widow's gift
   — — — —   Could be deaf as well
   — — — —   Played with a tambourine and
                      harp
   — — — —   Third Gospel
   — — — —   Similar
   — — — —   Sea or . . . of Galilee
   — — — —   No. 1's opposite

C.   H   O   P   E   Expect

— — — —   Nazareth was . . . to Jesus

— — — —   End of Paul's travels

— — — —   'She [Rahab] let them down by a . . . (Joshua 2)

— — — —   Head of the Roman Catholic Church

— — — —   Done for a photographer

— — — —   'Every night I [the lookout] stay at my . . .' (Isaiah 21)

— — — —   Price

— — — —   Son, coin and sheep in Luke 15

— — — —   Misplace

— — — —   Part of the ear

— — — —   Greater than No. 1 (1 Corinthians 13)

D.   S   A   N   D   Bad foundation

— — — —   Worn around the head or can produce music

— — — —   Britain is a '. . . of hope and glory'

— — — —   Narrow road

— — — —   Great dog

— — — —   Piece of glass

— — — —   Tree

— — — —   Not his for coal

— — — —   Fur

— — — —   He wears a habit

— — — —   Taunt

— — — —   Best foundation

76 : Bible Workers and Materials

Two words are printed in from the list below to start you off.

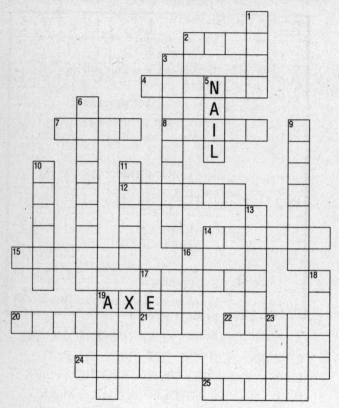

ANVIL   ARTIST   AXE   BAKER   BOAT
BRICK   BUILDER   CARPENTER   CLAY
DYER   FISHER   GOLDSMITH   IRON
MASON   NAIL   NET   PAINT   PAPER
PEN   PLOUGH   POTTER   SILVER
STONE   TAILOR   TANNER   WOOD
WRITER

The words appear forwards, backwards, upwards, downwards or diagonally. Join up the letters of each word.

B	M	U	R	C	E	L	S	I	E	V	E
E	Q	A	B	A	R	L	E	Y	O	A	F
A	F	L	O	U	R	E	L	O	P	T	I
N	I	L	W	E	T	V	A	U	R	I	N
O	S	A	L	T	T	I	C	M	I	L	K
V	H	B	S	A	R	L	S	C	I	R	W
E	K	A	B	M	D	O	P	N	O	N	A
N	E	L	R	O	X	L	U	F	E	L	T
Y	E	G	U	H	A	J	E	G	U	J	E
A	Z	G	E	T	O	D	I	S	H	K	R
P	H	R	E	S	O	E	O	L	A	M	P
C	H	A	I	R	S	P	I	C	E	F	D

ALOE   BARLEY   BEAN   BOWL   CAKE
CHAIRS   CREAM   CRUMB   CUP
DISH   DOUGH   FISH   FLOUR   FORK
JUG   KNIFE   LADLE   LAMP   MILK
MINT   OIL   OLIVE   OVEN   PLATE
POT   RUE   SALT   SCALES   SIEVE
SPICE   TABLE   TROUGH   VAT
WATER   YEAST

78 : Columns of Truth

Start the missing word in the square provided, as in the given example.

1. Easter message – 'He is . . .'

2. Jacob and . . .

3. Paul's conversion on the road to . . .

4. 'Your word, O Lord, is . . .' (Psalm 119)

5. Noon is also . . .

6. . . . and Silas   **P**

7. . . . commandments

8. Jeroboam, King of . . .

9. Jerusalem, Mount of . . .

10. . . . was a mighty hunter

   Column: Appears twice in Ephesians 1

B.

1. Heaven and . . .

2. The same . . . and today and for ever

3. . . . lamb

4. . . . of Bashan

5. To . . . favour (Proverbs 19)

6. . . . and a purifier of silver (Malachi 3)

7. Judas . . .

8. . . . offering

9. . . . doer

10. man . . .

   Column: How Jesus described some enquiring Pharisees

79 : Time of Elijah and Elisha

A. Rearrange each set of letters and discover a king's name.

1. N IS HIM   _____Jehu's father

2. OR JAM   _____He got rid of the sacred stone of Baal (2 Kings 3)

3. A H LAZE   _____Anointed by Elijah

4. HE OR JAM   _____Father of Jehosheba (2 Kings 11)

5. O HE HATH JAPS _____He built a fleet of trading ships (1 King 22)

6. HUJE   _____He drove like a madman (2 Kings 9)

7. A BED HAND   _____A king of Aram (1 Kings 20)

8. HA HA AZI   _____He fell from an upper room (2 Kings 1)

B. Rearrange each set of letters and discover a place name.

1. HIS BET   _____Home of Elijah

2. I AS A RAM   _____Capital of Israel

3. RECLAM   _____Mountain of Baal's defeat

4. RAZE H PATH   _____Home of a widow

5. GLADIATOR HEM _____Elisha went there with a flask of oil (2 Kings 9)

6. HER KIT   _____Where Elijah was fed by ravens

7. A SAD SCUM   _____City of Syria

8. SUM HEN   _____Where Elijah restored a boy to life

80 : Criss-Cross

The words appear forwards, backwards, upwards,
downwards or diagonally. Join up the letters of each word.
All words are from the Bible.

A. TRAVELLING ALONG

C	K	H	O	R	S	E
H	L	D	T	R	A	C
A	M	R	O	A	D	A
R	E	I	N	S	D	M
I	L	V	L	P	L	E
O	X	E	A	E	E	L
T	A	R	N	E	U	W
P	Q	R	E	D	I	R

AXLE   CAMEL   CART   CHARIOT   DRIVER
HORSE   LANE   MILE   REINS   RIDER   ROAD
SADDLE   SPEED

B. IN THE GARDEN

A	R	P	K	M	K	D
Z	I	L	N	V	R	D
C	D	A	I	O	O	N
F	E	N	O	O	F	U
R	E	T	B	D	S	O
U	W	R	E	R	I	R
I	O	E	Q	P	E	G
T	S	E	V	R	A	H

DIG   FORK   FRUIT   GROUND   HARVEST
HERB   PLANT   ROOT   SEED   SOIL   SOW
TREE   VINE   WEED

C. UP IN THE SKY

L	I	G	H	T	C	F
B	L	C	A	H	D	S
W	S	L	S	U	U	T
I	M	O	O	N	X	A
N	O	U	W	D	O	R
D	K	D	R	E	M	W
P	E	I	Z	R	H	K
E	B	R	A	I	N	J

BIRD CLOUD LIGHT MOON RAIN RED
(sky) SMOKE SNOW STAR SUN THUNDER
WIND

D. WHAT SHALL WE EAT AND DRINK?

E	T	S	U	C	O	L
F	I	S	H	H	R	M
I	U	D	A	E	R	B
G	R	W	T	E	E	T
R	F	A	K	S	T	Q
A	W	A	L	E	T	P
P	C	G	I	L	U	B
E	H	U	M	K	B	A

BREAD BUTTER CAKE CHEESE FIG FISH
FRUIT GRAPE LOCUST MILK WATER

81 : Odd Man Out

Underline the name or word that does not fit in with the other two in each line.

A.

1. Jerusalem, London, Rome
2. Onion, cucumber, potato
3. Herod, Asa, Jehu
4. Colossians, Romans, Jude
5. Mulberry, chestnut, oak
6. Orange, apple, fig
7. Red, Salt, Caspian
8. Danube, Pharpar, Jordan
9. Abel, Cain, Joshua
10. Iron, lead, platinum

B.

1. Elephant, lion, fox
2. Lamp, torch, gas
3. Shem, Ham, Joseph
4. Levi, Gad, Zulu
5. Livingstone, Roosevelt, Carey
6. Lily, crocus, tulip
7. Red, mauve, yellow
8. Ziv, Bul, April
9. Synagogue, palace, temple
10. Snowdon, Seir, Sinai

Each word is found in 1 John 1:5–10.

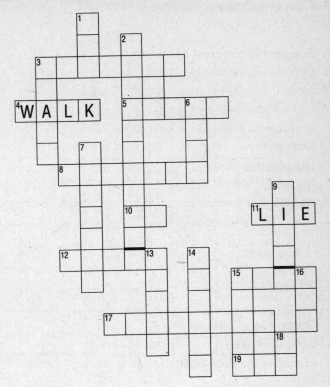

83 : 'S's All

Mark with crosses the squares which correspond with lines and columns. One example is given and there is one column too many.

	A SOLOMON	B SAMUEL	C SAMSON	D SIMEON	E SHADRACH	F STEPHEN	G SAPPHIRA	H SAUL	I SENNACHERIB	J SOSTHENES	K SISERA
1. First martyr											
2. Also called Niger											
3. Strong man											
4. Saved from a firey furnace				X							
5. Prophet											
6. Synagogue ruler											
7. Canaanite army commander											
8. King of Israel											
9. Converted near Damascus											
10. Wife of Ananias											

Fill in the spaces according to the clues. The last letter or letters of answer No. 1 are the same as the first letter or letters of answer No. 2, and so on. Each new word starts a new circle.

A.
1. Tribe of Israel
2. 'God created man in his own . . .'
3. Pethahiah held this position in the Persian king's office (Nehemiah 11)
4. Mountain which sings for joy with Hermon (Psalm 89)
5. Constellation mentioned by Job (chapter 9) and Amos
6. One and . . .
7. Visited by Paul and twinned with Derbe (Acts 16)

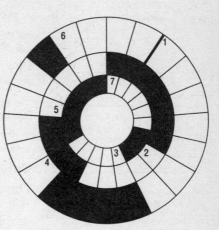

B.
1. Nebuchadnezzar threw three men in as it blazed away
2. Tree especially in Lebanon
3. Used with spears and javelins for fighting
4. The devil
5. Women of Zion wore a chain on this part of the body
6. Jacob's first wife
7. Father of Baasha, King of Israel; also a prophet of Shiloh (1 Kings 11)

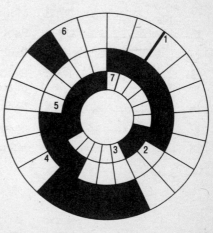

85 : More Six-Letter Names

Notice the order in which the given letters are arranged, then add the first three letters of each name.

1. _____ AEL — Anointed King of Aram by Elijah

2. _____ BUS — A prophet of Jerusalem

3. _____ CAS — Robe-maker also called Tabitha

4. _____ DOD — City of the Philistines where they worshipped Dagon

5. _____ EON — He beat the Midianites with 300 men

6. _____ GAL — Where the Israelites erected a twelve-stone memorial

7. _____ HER — Queen of Zerxes

8. _____ ILA — Priscilla's husband

9. _____ JAH — Prophet who wore a hair coat and leather belt

10. _____ LEK — Grandson of Esau (Genesis 36)

11. _____ MON — Mountain

12. _____ NAH — Mother of Samuel

13. _____ OAM — Pool in Jerusalem

14. _____ PUS — Paul left his cloak with him

15. _____ RAM — Descendant of Benjamin (Numbers 26)

16. _____ SIA — Now called Iran

17. _____ TUS — Successor to Felix

18. _____ UCH — Jeremiah's scribe

Write the answers to clues A to E in the semicircles, then transfer the letters to the strips. This will give you a promise of Jesus. One example is given to help you.

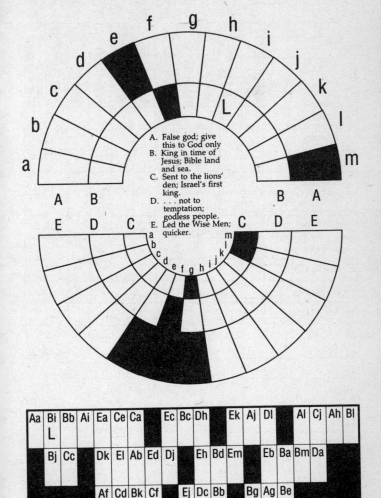

A. False god; give this to God only
B. King in time of Jesus; Bible land and sea.
C. Sent to the lions' den; Israel's first king.
D. . . . not to temptation; godless people.
E. Led the Wise Men; quicker.

95

87 : A Podful of 'P's

Mark with crosses the squares which correspond with lines and columns. One example is given and there is one column too many.

	A Where Jacob met God	B Tax-collector	C Apostle	D Fisherman	E Aquila's wife	F Epistle	G Apostle; evangelist	H King of Egypt	I Governor	J Sister in Cenchrea	K Captain of Pharaoh's guard
1. Paul											
2. Peter				X							
3. Pilate											
4. Peniel											
5. Pharaoh											
6. Philemon											
7. Philip											
8. Phoebe											
9. Potiphar											
10. Priscilla											

This is a criss-cross puzzle after the pattern of Quiz 77. All the clues below are Bible words.

P	L	E	N	T	I	L	C	P	H	D	F
O	I	Z	U	F	L	O	U	R	A	L	G
M	U	S	T	A	R	D	R	D	Y	R	I
E	I	N	T	N	H	Y	R	J	A	I	F
G	O	L	O	A	M	U	A	P	P	L	E
R	Y	A	K	M	C	D	E	E	S	O	V
A	E	E	S	E	E	H	C	Q	L	N	I
N	C	T	N	P	E	L	I	A	R	O	L
A	O	K	T	O	E	L	P	O	L	I	O
T	W	L	Y	U	H	L	S	W	I	N	E
E	N	A	E	B	B	D	T	T	A	O	G
C	D	N	O	M	L	A	M	B	B	M	G

ALMOND   ALOE   APPLE   BEAN
BUTTER   CHEESE   CORN   COW
CURD   FIG   FLOUR   GOAT   GRAPE
HAY   HONEY   LAMB   LEEK   LEMON
LENTIL   MELON   MILK   MUSTARD
MYRRH   NUT   OIL   OLIVE   ONION
PISTACHIO   POMEGRANATE   SEED
SPELT   SPICE   WINE

For each answer add the verse number in the circle provided.

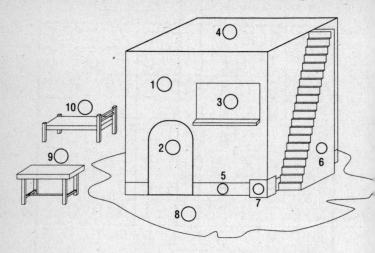

1. Ananias was a whitewashed one (Acts 23)
2. Opened for him who knocks (Luke 11)
3. Eutychus sat here (Acts 20)
4. Where Peter prayed (Acts 10)
5. Where a poor man might sit (James 2)
6. Portico was reached by these (Ezekiel 40)
7. Jesus Christ is the chief (Ephesians 2)
8. Should be on rock (Matthew 7)
9. Where Jesus reclined (Luke 7)
10. Where a Greek woman found her healed child lying (Mark 7)

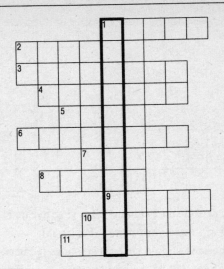

1. Where Jonah found a ship

2. By what small thing is a large ship steered? (James 3)

3. A good wife is like this sort of ship (Proverbs 31)

4. Who built ships at Ezion Geber? (1 Kings 9)

5. What people will be frightened by messengers in ships? (Ezekiel 30)

6. Ships from here were shattered by an east wind (Psalm 48)

7. Who lingered by the ships? (Judges 5)

8. Where would the Lord send the disobedient in ships? (Deuteronomy 28)

9. He brought gold in ships (1 Kings 10)

10. On to what island was Paul shipwrecked? (Acts 28)

11. Where did Paul find a ship for Phoenicia? (Acts 21)

Centre column: Who had a fleet of sailing ships which never set sail? (1 Kings 22)

91 : Bible Singing

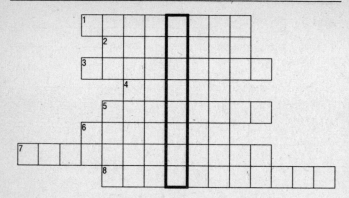

1. In what prison did Paul and Silas sing hymns?

2. 'I will sing . . . to your name' (Psalm 18)

3. The Ephesians should sing these songs (Ephesians 5)

4. In Tyre there will be 'an end to your . . . songs' (Ezekiel 26)

5. God's people burst into this song (Psalm 98)

6. When God rejected Israel there were no . . . songs (Psalm 78)

7. Jonah's song was one of . . . (Jonah 2)

8. David was surrounded by songs of . . . (Psalm 32)

You will see that the centre column has a certain unity.

92 : Lost Strings and Sounds of Music

Add the missing word in each verse.

1. It is good to praise the Lord and make _____
   to your name (Psalm 92)

2. There on the poplars we hung our _____
   (Psalm 137)

3. Make music to him on the ten-stringed _____
   (Psalm 33)

4. Praise him with the _____ and flute
   (Psalm 150)

5. As soon as you hear the sound of the horn,
   flute _____ lyre, harp, pipes and all kinds of
   music, you must fall down and worship (Daniel 3)

6. Sound the ram's _____ at the New Moon
   (Psalm 81)

7. If the _____ does not sound a clear call, who
   will get ready for battle? (1 Corinthians 14)

8. Miriam the prophetess, Aaron's sister, took
   a _____ in her hand (Exodus 15)

93 : Anglican Cathedrals

Locate the Anglican cathedrals by adding the figures in the squares provided.

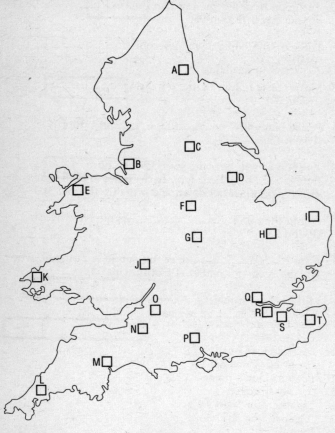

1. Coventry
2. Durham
3. Canterbury
4. Salisbury
5. Norwich
6. Ely
7. Truro

8. Bristol
9. Hereford
10. Liverpool
11. Wakefield
12. Bangor
13. Southwark
14. Exeter

15. Wells
16. Lichfield
17. Rochester
18. St. Paul's
19. St. Davids
20. Lincoln

Each word is linked by one of three letters.

1. When Elijah taunted Baal's prophets (1 Kings 18)
2. Tree at Shechem (Genesis 35)
3. To know in Scotland
4. Finish
5. (Across) Dig
5. (Down) She gathers her chicks (Matthew 23)
6. Chick's first home
7. First light
8. Limb
9. Nation's condition after drinking wine (Jeremiah 51)
10. Tree, burnt remains
11. Time of darkness
12. Goes with Magog
13. (Across) Unclean to Israelites
13. (Down) Dug for Jeremiah
14. Highest point
15. Tightens the loom (Judges 16)
16. (Across) Can be breached (Proverbs 17)
16. (Down) Lion's home
17. '. . . has broken'
18. No room for Jesus here
19. 'Hushed was the . . . hymn'

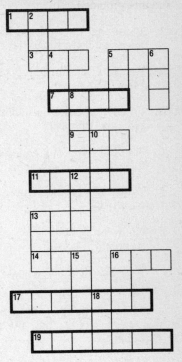

95 : Missing Words

Fill in the missing words and you will find that each answer describes a movement.

1. 'Those that have jointed legs for _____ on the ground' (Leviticus 11)

2. 'He _____ to his feet and came to Jesus' (Mark 10)

3. 'Whoever follows me will never _____ in darkness' (John 8)

4. 'Rejoice in that day and _____ for joy' (Luke 6)

5. 'They will _____ and not grow weary' (Isaiah 40)

6. 'He ordered those who could _____ to jump overboard' (Acts 27)

7. 'They lick dust like a snake, like creatures that _____ on the ground' (Micah 7)

8. 'Anyone who does not carry his cross and _____ me cannot be my disciple' (Luke 14)

9. 'Let the water teem with living creatures, and let birds _____ above the earth' (Genesis 1)

10. 'If a blind man leads a blind man, both will _____ into a pit' (Matthew 15)

11. 'In your majesty _____ forth victoriously on behalf of truth' (Psalm 45)

12. 'Resist the devil, and he will _____ from you' (James 4)

All answers are to be found in 1 Kings 18:16–46.

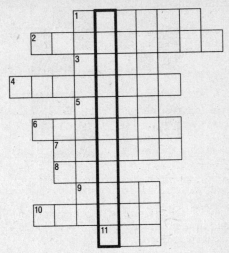

1. The prophets of Baal slashed themselves with these
2. Offered on Carmel
3. When Elijah's taunts began
4. 'Maybe he [Baal] is . . .
5. King of Israel in Elijah's time
6. He had four hundred false prophets
7. Valley of slaughter
8. It grew black
9. It burned Elijah's sacrifice
10. With them Elijah built an altar
11. On Carmel he was proved to be the one and only

   Centre column: The prophets of Baal were frantic in this
   action

97 : Eight Nines

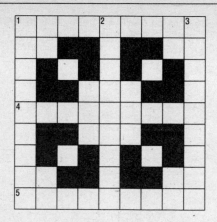

ACROSS

1. 'Being fully . . . that God had power' (Romans 4)
4. Dangerous in a drunkard's hand (Proverbs 26)
5. Welsh national park

DOWN

1. Offered with prayers (Hebrews 5)
2. Brought under trades union rules
3. Blue flowers like larkspur

DIAGONALLY

1. The persecuted travelled this far with Stephen (Acts 11)
5. If a thief 'is caught, he must pay . . .' (Proverbs 6)

Write the answers to clues A to D in the semi-circles, then transfer the letters to the strips. This will give you the words often used at the end of a service. One example is given to help.

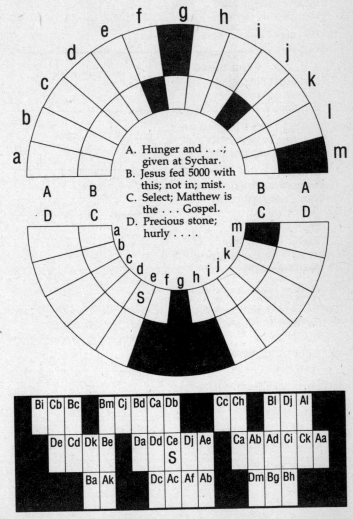

A. Hunger and . . .; given at Sychar.
B. Jesus fed 5000 with this; not in; mist.
C. Select; Matthew is the . . . Gospel.
D. Precious stone; hurly . . . .

99 : Weights, Measures and Coins

As you work through these clues you will see a pattern developing.

1. An ancient vessel whose measurements are recorded in Genesis _____

2. Weight of a gold nose ring (Genesis 24) _____

3. A quarter of this of seed pods cost five shekels during a famine in Samaria (2 Kings 6) _____

4. Sorcery scrolls burned in Ephesus were worth fifty thousand of these (Acts 19) _____

5. Gideon made bread with an . . . of flour (Judges 6) _____

6. The water beneath Paul's ship in the Adriatic Sea was ninety deep (Acts 27) _____

7. Twenty make a shekel (Ezekiel 45) _____

8. A measure for oil in Ezekiel 46 _____

9. Eighteen of these equal a cubit (Genesis 6) _____

10. They held twenty to thirty gallons each in Cana (John 2) _____

11. Small English barrel about ten gallons _____

12. A measure for oil in Leviticus 14 _____

13. Emmaus was about
    seven from Jerusalem
    (Luke 24)   _____

14. Bible river over 3,000
    miles in its full length   _____

15. Amount of manna to
    be kept for
    generations to come
    (Exodus 16)   _____

16. About a quarter of an
    ounce (1 Samuel 13,
    margin)   _____

17. Saul's servant had
    this part of a shekel
    of silver (1 Samuel 9)   _____

18. She threshed an
    ephah of barley in the
    field of Boaz   _____

19. A weight associated
    with the sanctuary
    (Numbers 7)   _____

20. A weight and an
    aptitude   _____

100 : Crossword

ACROSS

1. Works with the ploughman (1 Corinthians 9)
5. Preposition
7. Paul was proud to be one (Romans 11)
11. Indian coin
12. Rough crowd
13. King of Judah
14. Enemy
16. Scottish boy
18. 'Eternal, immortal . . . the only God' (1 Timothy 1)
20. Christian teaching in school
21. Where you shine like stars (Philippians 2)

DOWN

1. Outing
2. Unusual
3. Greek letter
4. Place of twelve springs (Exodus 15)
6. Spun by a spider
8. Paired with Tyre
9. Relieves
10. All
14. 'Let us . . . our eyes on Jesus' (Hebrews 12)
15. Level
16. Headless river in Rome

Answers

Quiz 1 : Crossword

ACROSS 1. Sales 6. Palestine
10. Call 11. Canes 12. Oiv
13. Magnet 14. Oral
16. Pna (Nap) 17. Ti
18. Eater 21. Sligo
23. Tema 24. Oioh 25. Ai
26. In 27. Pentecost
30. Spent
DOWN 1. Salvation 2. All
3. Le 4. Escape
5. Stagnation 6. Pair
7. Innate 8. Nee 9. (N)est
10. Coo 15. Lights 19. Emit
20. Ran 21. Sop 22. Lie
25. Ace 28. Ep 29. St

Quiz 2 : Bible Dreams

1. Pharaoh 2. Laban
3. Wise 4. Solomon
5. Joseph 6. Pilate 7. Cares
8. Jacob 9. Night
Centre column: Abimelech

Quiz 3 : Regroup the Letters

1. Psalm 8:9
2. John 6:37
3. 1 Thessalonians 5:13
4. Psalm 7:10
5. 1 Timothy 6:6
6. Psalm 29:11
7. 1 Peter 5:7

Quiz 4 : Same for Three

1. Hand 2. Foot 3. Off
4. Life 5. God 6. Free
7. Man 8. Water 9. Cross
10. Door/Gate 11. High
12. Ever

Quiz 5 : Eight Bible Gates

1. Adullam 2. Boaz
3. Crippled (verse 2)
4. Damascus (verse 5)
5. Elders (verse 19) 6. Flood
(verse 10) 7. Guard (verse 39)
8. Horse (verse 28)

Quiz 6 : In All Directions

A.

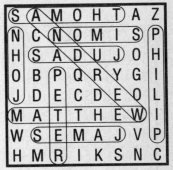

B.

C.

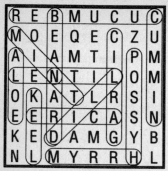

Quiz 9 : Let's Go to Work

1. Embalmers 2. Fuller
3. Weaver 4. Bricks
5. Baker 6. Masons
7. Tentmaker 8. Spindle
9. Potter 10. Matthew
Centre column: Blacksmith

Quiz 10 : Ten Full Urns

1. Burnt 2. Churning
3. Furnace 4. Journey
5. Laburnum 6. Mourn
7. Nocturnal 8. Return
9. Spurn 10. Turn

D.

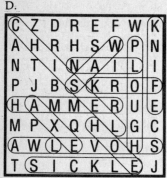

Quiz 11 : Sailing Away

1. Boat 2. Deck 3. Oars
4. Jonah 5. Mast 6. Tyre
7. Kittim 8. Storm 9. Pilot
10. Rudder 11. Solomon
Centre column: Adramyttium

Quiz 12 : Lost Words

'Look . . . world' (John 1:29)

Quiz 13 : Jumbled Countries

1. Persia 2. Cyprus 3. Egypt
4. Phrygia 5. Pamphylia
6. Macedonia 7. Ethiopia
8. Assyria 9. Crete
10. Cappadocia

Quiz 7 : Who Are We?

A. Philemon B. Matthias
C. Thyatira D. Benjamin

Quiz 8 : Crossword

ACROSS 2. Tis 6. Abraham
9. Goa 10. Asa 11. Ill
13. Galilee 16. Stephen
21. Via 22. Ara 24. Bar
26. Nodding 28. Eat
DOWN 1. Magog 2. Trail
3. (D)ia(1) 4. Shall
5. Amaze 7. Bo 8. As
12. Li 14. Act 15. Eve
16. Swans 17. Evade 18. Pi
19. Habit 20. Norge
23. Ro(ad) 25. An 27. Da

Quiz 14 : Pyramids

A.
1. A 2. As 3. Sea 4. Esau
5. Sauce 6. Causes 7. Case

B.
1. O 2. To 3. Not 4. Tons
5. Stone 6. Honest 7. Toes

Quiz 15 : Limericks

A. Nain, Cheer B. Jesus,
Beatitudes C. Barnabas,
Lystra D. Athens, Altar

Quiz 16 : Changing Letters

A. CORN
    MORN
    MOAN
    LOAN
    LOAF

C. COLD
    HOLD
    HELD
    HEAD
    HEAT

B. GAIN
    CAIN
    COIN
    LOIN
    LOIS
    LOSS

Quiz 17 : Regroup More Letters

1. Ephesians 5:2
2. Psalm 28:7
3. Galatians 6:10
4. Job 5:17
5. Matthew 6:33
6. James 5:16
7. Psalm 27:1

Quiz 18 : A Bible Wardrobe

1. Dress 2. Camel 3. Robes
4. Charms 5. Wool
6. Tiaras 7. Sandals 8. Cape
9. Purple 10. Linen 11. Body
Centre column: Embroidered

Quiz 19 : Names and Places

Adam Babel Canaan
Decapolis Egypt Felix
Gideon Herod Isaiah
Japheth Kish Lazarus
Mysia Noah Ophir Peter
Quails Rebekah Samaritan
Timothy Uriah Vineyard
Widow Xerves Yellow
Zebedee

Quiz 20 : Add the Figures

1. 12 2. 1 3. 40 4. 2 5. 3
6. 8 7. 5 8. 6 9. 9 10. 30
11. 4 12. 10

Quiz 21 : In the Desert

1. Highway 2. Quails
3. Calf 4. Judea 5. Kadesh
6. Korah 7. Manna 8. Red
9. Moses 10. Passover
Centre column: Wilderness

Quiz 22 : Eleven Lots

1. Allotment 2. Aloth
3. Blot 4. Cloth 5. Lotan
6. Lotion 7. Lotus
8. Mikloth 9. Pilot 10. Plot
11. Zealot

Quiz 23 : Mini-Crosswords

A. ACROSS 1. Hit 3. Man
    5. Ate 7. Art (verse 7)
    9. End (verse 6) 10. All
    11. Din (verse 55)
    DOWN 1. Ham 2. Ten
    4. Ant (verse 6) 5. Ada
    6. Eel 7. Add (verse 5)
    8. Tin (verse 22)

B. ACROSS 1. Can 3. Oct
    5. Axe (verse 10) 7. Aim
    (verse 11) 9. Lot
    10. Sum 11. Ear
    DOWN 1. Coo 2. Not
    4. Cox 5. Ass 6. Elm
    7. Ate 8. Mar

C. ACROSS 1. Tan 3. Rod
    5. Ben 7. Saw 9. Oak
    10. War 11. Yen
    DOWN 1. Tar 2. Nod
    4. One 5. Bow 6. Nor
    7. Sky 8. Win

Quiz 24 : Strip Words

A. Lebanon B. Syracuse
C. Capernaum
D. Samothrace
E. Mesopotamia
F. Philadelphia

Quiz 25 : Wells and Springs

1. Beersheba 2. Baca
3. Bethlehem 4. Ravines
5. Parched 6. Righteous
7. Sirah 8. Jacob 9. Princes
Centre column: Salvation

Quiz 26 : Things in Common

A. 1. Seas 2. Kings of Israel
3. Towns in Galilee
4. Parables of Jesus
5. Missionaries 6. Sons of
Jacob 7. Founders of Christian
organizations 8. Parts of a
church 9. New Testament
books 10. Hometown was
Bethsaida

B. 1. Sons of Noah 2. Wise
men's gifts to Jesus
3. Churches in the Revelation
4. Cathedral cities 5. Kings of
Judah 6. Prophets 7. Rivers
flowing from Eden 8. Musical
instruments of Daniel 3
9. Mountains 10. Lights in
the sky

Quiz 27 ' Psalm Forty-Six

1. Quake 2. Of
3. Mountains 4. Foam
5. Roar 6. River 7. (Across)
Are; (Down) Almighty
8. (Across) In; (Down) Is
9. Streams 10. Uproar
11. Most 12. Strength
13. Earth 14. Dwells
15. Fortress 16. Waters
17. He 18. And 19. Not
20. Melts

Quiz 28 : Hidden Bible Birds

1. Dove 2. Heron 3. Hen
4. Kite 5. Thrushes 6. Stork
7. Owl 8. Raven 9. Gull
10. Swallow

Quiz 29 : Make the Trio

1. Ham 2. Myrrh 3. Noon
4. Father 5. Greek
6. Shadrach 7. Water 8. Eat
9. Love 10. Truth 11. Mene

Quiz 30 : The First Psalm

1. Blessed 2. Planted
3. Season 4. Seat
5. Prospers 6. Perish
7. Streams 8. Righteous
9. (Across) Meditates; (Down)
Mockers 10. (Across) Tree;
(Down) Therefore
11. Delight 12. Man
13. Like 14. Wind
15. Sinners 16. Blows
17. Does 18. Leaf

Quiz 31 : Hidden Bible Rivers

1. Abana 2. Jordan
3. Habor 4. Ebar 5. Pishon
6. Pharpar 7. Arnon
8. Gihon

Quiz 32 : Low But Not Out

1. Bellows 2. Blowing
3. Fallow 4. Flowers
5. Flowing 6. Follow
7. Glowing 8. Hallowed
9. Hollow 10. Lowing
11. Mellow 12. Shallow
13. Slow 14. Swallow

Quiz 33 : Rearrange and Add

1. Blameless 2. Comparison
3. Breastplate
4. Gentleness 5. Pentecost
6. Testifies 7. Hypocrisy
8. Considered 9. Orphans
10. Discipline 11. Respect
12. Thornbushes

Quiz 34 : The Hundredth Psalm

1. Faithfulness 2. Earth
3. Thanks 4. Sheep
5. Shout 6. Good 7. (Across)
Ever; (Down) Endures
8. Know 9. Us 10. Name
11. Courts 12. Worship
13. People 14. Are 15. For
16. Pasture 17. All
18. Enter 19. Love 20. The
21. Before

Quiz 35 : Help in Time of Need

1. Afraid 2. Braid 3. Inlaid
4. Laid 5. Maid 6. Mislaid
7. Paid 8. Raid 9. Said
10. Staid

Quiz 36 : Bible Places

1. Israel 2. Cyprus
3. Ashdod 4. Carmel
5. Jordan 6. Hebron
7. Lystra 8. Rhodes
9. Pisgah 10. Sychar
11. Emmaus 12. Paphos
13. Arabia 14. Smyrna
15. Ziklag 16. Sardis
17. Bashan 18. Gilboa
19. Cyrene 20. Gilead

Quiz 37 : Bible People

1. Samuel 2. Thomas
3. Joseph 4. Abijam
5. Haggai 6. Esther
7. Joshua 8. Lamech
9. Aquila 10. Eunice
11. Samson 12. Philip
13. Shemer 14. Hanani
15. Darius 16. Reuben
17. Xerxes 18. Baasha
19. Bildad 20. Pilate

Quiz 38 : The Traders Are Coming

1. Shekels 2. Purple
3. Scales 4. Tarshish
5. Caravans 6. Lebanon
7. Gold 8. Chariot 9. Horses
Centre column: Merchandise

Quiz 39 : Outspoken Prophets

1. Elijah 2. Ezekiel 3. Aaron
4. Oded 5. Samuel
6. Ahijah 7. Agabus
8. Nahum 9. Shemaiah
10. Noah 11. Elisha 12. Joel
13. Hosea
Centre column: (a) Jeremiah;
            (b) Moses

Quiz 40 : Seven-Letter Words

A. 1. Matthew 2. Weather
3. Royalty 4. Yielded
5. Deliver 6. Revenge
7. Eliakim

B. 1. Grumble 2. Ephesus
3. Solomon 4. Nothing
5. Galilee 6. Emperor
7. Reaping

C. 1. Apollos 2. Samaria
3. Antioch 4. Heathen
5. Nineveh 6. Harvest
7. Talitha

Quiz 41 : Metals and Minerals

1. Salt 2. Sand 3. Soda
4. Clay 5. Lead 6. Silver
7. Tin 8. Bitumen 9. Gold
10. Iron 11. Copper
12. Bronze
Centre column: 'A's, 'I's and 'O's

Quiz 42 : Crossword

ACROSS 1. Solomon 6. Eat
7. Oversee 8. Sisters
11. Message (verse 18)
15. Isobars 17. Nur (Run)
18. Teenage
DOWN 1. Scots 2. Leeds
3. Oar 4. Mtsae (Meats)
5. Needs 9. Ice 10. Rag
11. Moist 12. Stone
13. Abana 14. Elsie 16. Bun

Quiz 43 : Parents and Children

1. Adam 2. Ahaz 3. Asher
4. Amaziah 5. Jacob 6. Saul
7. Caleb 8. Samuel 9. David
10. Boaz 11. Noah
12. Isaiah 13. Maacah

Quiz 44 : Twos and Threes

A. Italy Jonah Peter Silas
Malta Sidon James Jacob
Laban Crete Egypt Derbe

B. Judas David Titus
Herod Asher Chloe Jesse
Joash Marah Ophir Samos
Tubal

Quiz 45 : The Fourth Commandment

1. Six 2. Sea 3. Manservant
4. But 5. Animals 6. Work
7. Shall 8. Labour 9. Or
10. Remember 11. Made
12. Daughter 13. Earth
14. Not 15. Alien
16. Blessed 17. Gates
18. Lord 19. Rested 20. The
21. Seventh 22. Holy 23. To
24. Do 25. By

Quiz 46 : More Names and Places

Abigail Bethel Crete
Deborah Elisha Festus
Gilboa Hermon Isaac Joash
Kidron Lamech Malachi
Naboth Og Persia Quartus
Romans Shechem Tarsus
Ur Vashti Winter (E)xodus
Youths Zalmon

Quiz 47 : Harvest Festival

1. Crop 2. Sickle 3. Sower
4. Locusts 5. Grain
6. Thunder 7. Thistles
8. Plants 9. Wages
Centre Column: Ploughing

Quiz 48 : Threes and Fours

A. Samaria Joseph Dorcas
Ananias Athens Calvary
Nazareth Samuel Canaan
Sardis Antioch Sapphira

B. Cyprus Lystra Tarshish
Festus Jordan Elijah
Hannah Eunice Arabia
Salamis Bethany Gideon

Quiz 49 : More Pyramids

A. 1. E 2. Et 3. Set 4. Rest
5. Tears 6. Easter 7. Star

B. 1. I 2. Is 3. Sit 4. Slit
5. Stile 6. Titles 7. List

C. 1. U 2. Ur 3. Run
4. Burn 5. Urban 6. Turban
7. Aunt

Quiz 50 : Land of Egypt

1. Straw 2. Miriam
3. Rameses 4. Aswan
5. Moses 6. Locusts
7. Pharaoh 8. Joseph
9. Passover
Centre column: Treasures

Quiz 51 : Framed Verses

A.
1. 'I . . . life' (verse 35)
2. 'Come . . . rest' (verse 28)
3. 'The . . . want' (verse 1)
4. 'The . . . afraid' (verse 6)
5. 'God is love' (verse 16)
6. 'Love one another' (verse 34)
7. 'He . . . fortress' (verse 2)

B.
1. 'Be . . . God' (verse 10)
2. 'Humble . . . up' (verse 10)
3. 'In . . . us' (verse 37)
4. 'Put . . . schemes' (verse 11) 5. 'Honour . . . mother' (verse 2)

C.
1. 'You . . . neighbour' (verse 16)
2. 'Blessed . . . God' (verse 8)
3. 'Prepare . . . him' (verse 4)
4. 'The . . . it' (verse 1)
5. 'Every . . . above' (verse 17)
6. 'Let . . . Lord' (verse 6)

Quiz 52 : Who Are We Again?

A. Bethany B. Jericho
C. Nazareth D. Galilee

Quiz 53 : Naaman Visits the Prophet

1. Peace 2. Robes 3. Wash
4. Angry 5. Gehazi
6. Leprosy 7. Elisha
8. Aramean 9. Jordan
10. Stopped 11. Cleansed
12. Girl

Centre column : Abana Pharpar

Quiz 54 : Bible Lands and Provinces

ANSWERS 54

Quiz 55 : Ten Tents

1. Intent 2. Contentment
3. Detention 4. Attention
5. Potent 6. Extent
7. Competent 8. Penitent
9. Tenth 10. Portent

Quiz 56 : Six-Letter Names

1. Ophrah 2. Bozrah
3. Abiram 4. Ararat
5. Andrew 6. Hebrew
7. Nimrod 8. Kidron
9. Ephron 10. Hebron
11. Cyprus 12. Jairus

Quiz 57 : Linking Up

A. Matthew, Mark, Luke, John, Revelation, Peter, Jude, Titus, Colossians, James, Philemon, Timothy·

B. Jacob, Moses, Gideon, David, Noah, Abram, Isaac, Balaam, Samuel, Joshua

Quiz 58 : All in the Family

1. Mark 2. Mary 3. Aaron
4. David 5. Isaac 6. Martha
7. Naomi 8. Lamech
9. Benjamin 10. Rachel
11. Saul 12. Dinah

Quiz 59 : All in the Wardrobe

1. Turban 2. Linen
3. Sandals 4. Veil 5. Tiara
6. Change 7. Shawl 8. Robe
9. Camels 10. Capes
11. Tunic 12. Belt
Centre column: Undergarment

Quiz 60 : Threes and Sevens

A. ACROSS 2. Old 5. Pay
6. Web 9. Hebrews 13. Ego
14. Gnu 15. Ham
DOWN 1. Top 3. Law
4. Dye 7. Bar 8. She
10. Egg 11. Bon 12. Sea

B. ACROSS 2. Wet 5. Ear
6. Tin 9. Obadiah 13. Gap
14. Net 15. Spa
DOWN 1. Owe 3. Eat 4. Tri
7. Nod 8. Fog 10. Ban
11. Ape 12. Hip

C. ACROSS 2. Asa 5. Yes
6. Thy 9. Earnest 13. Any
14. Ten 15. Low
DOWN 1. Hay 3. Set 4. Ash
7. Yen 8. Pea 10. Ant
11. Rye 12. Two

Quiz 61 : The Shepherd's Psalm

1. Guides 2. Death
3. House 4. Lord
5. Presence
6. Righteousness 7. Surely
8. Pastures 9. Shepherd
10. In 11. Green 12. Dwell
13. Cup 14. The
15. Shadow 16. Beside
17. Ever 18. Prepare
19. Rod 20. Paths 21. Oil
22. Head 23. Love 24. Days

Quiz 62 : Crossword on Horeb

ACROSS 1. Covenant
6. Aram 8. Eta 10. AM
11. (Eli)Sha 13. UK
14. Voice 16. To 17. Ere
20. Powerful
DOWN 2. Very 3. Nimshi
4. None 5. Quake 7. Earth
9. Tu 11. Son 12. Ace
15. Erif (fire) 18. Go 19. Ye

Quiz 63 : Bible Altars

1. Damascus 2. Isaac
3. Incense 4. Ophrah
5. Foreign 6. Fire 7. Gadites
8. Acacia 9. Athens
Centre column: Sacrifice

Quiz 64 : Collective Nouns

1. Rebels (24) 2. Vipers (7)
3. Hyssop (22) 4. Grapes
(23) 5. Livestock (38)
6. Soldiers (3 or 12) 7. Sheep
(31) 8. Ruins (37) 9. Pigs
(11) 10. Angels (13–15)
11. Rubble (11) 12. Locusts (14)

Quiz 65 : Muddled Verses

1. Verse 6 2. Verse 1 3. Verse
3 4. Verse 13 5. Verse 9
6. Verse 6 7. Verse 9 8. Verse
20 9. Verse 5 10. Verse 3
11. Verse 8 12. Verse 6

Quiz 66 : Four Directions

1. Northern 2. Old 3. Ran
4. Did 5. Ink 6. Nod
7. Dim 8. Key 9. Ewe
10. Eastern 11. Ask
12. End 13. (Across) Ark;
(Down) Awl 14. Dan
15. New 16. All 17. Log
18. Low 19. Gad 20. Dew
21. Western 22. Eli 23. Red
24. Ice 25. Cos 26. Win
27. Southern

Quiz 67 : Squares of Nine

A.
1. Zacchaeus 2. Testimony
3. Nicodemus 4. Samaritan
5. Beelzebub 6. Atonement
7. Zephaniah 8. Ephesians
Centre: Disciples

B.
9. Bethlehem 10. Salvation
11. Palestine 12. Decapolis
13. Macedonia 14. Jerusalem
15. Capernaum 16. Illyricum
Centre: Ptolemais

Quiz 68 : Men and Women of the Bible

A.
1. Ham 2. Naboth 3. Jacob
4. Andrew 5. Eliezer
6. Rufus 7. Haggai
8. Nathan 9. Isaiah
10. Abijah

B.
1. Abigail 2. Esther
3. Miriam 4. Jezebel
5. Rebekah 6. Zillah
7. Naomi 8. Dinah
9. Deborah 10. Purple

Quiz 69 : Wheels of Knowledge

A.
1. Jericho 2. Hosea 3. Seals
4. Sceva 5. Valid 6. Idol
7. Olives

B.
1. Puteoli 2. Lines 3. Nests
4. Silas 5. Ashes 6. Esau
7. Autumn

Quiz 70 : Flags of Bible Lands

1. Turkey, Lebanon, Malta
2. Iraq, Egypt, Syria
3. Jordan 4. Iran, Italy
5. Ethiopia 6. Greece, Israel
7. Cyprus

Quiz 71 : By the Window

1. Thieves 2. Jehu 3. Lattice
4. Prayed 5. Jericho
6. Noah 7. Paul 8. Clerestory
Centre column: Eutychus

Quiz 72 : Round We Go

A.
1. Joseph 2. Ephah 3. Ahab
4. Abel 5. Eli 6. Italy
7. Lydda 8. Dan 9. Naomi

B.
1. Jordan 2. Dance 3. Cell
4. Llan 5. Ant 6. Taxed
7. Edwin 8. Ink 9. Kneel

C.
1. Esther 2. Herod 3. Oded
4. Edge 5. Gem 6. Malta
7. Table 8. Leg 9. Grape

Quiz 73 : Twenty Broken Verses

1. Altars 2. Bread
3. Covenant 4. Dam
5. Earth 6. Faith 7. Gates
8. Heart 9. Iron 10. Jar
11. Law 12. Nations
13. Oath 14. Pottery
15. Rod 16. Scripture
17. Tablets
18. Unploughed 19. Wall
20. Yoke

Quiz 74 : Catching Fish

1. Night 2. Hook 3. Line
4. (Across) Solomon; (Down)
Sea 5. Lake 6. Galilee
7. Jonah 8. Catch 9. Deep
10. Andrew 11. Water
12. Zebedee 13. Net
14. Spear 15. Coin
16. Israel 17. Peter 18. Men
19. Boat 20. River 21. Broiled

Quiz 75 : Changing Letters

A.	B.
MORE	GIVE
CORE	GAVE
COME	RAVE
DOME	RATE
DIME	MATE
TIME	MITE
LIME	MUTE
LIMP	LUTE
LISP	LUKE
LIST	LIKE
LEST	LAKE
LESS	TAKE

C.	D.
HOPE	SAND
HOME	BAND
ROME	LAND
ROPE	LANE
POPE	DANE
POSE	PANE
POST	PINE
COST	MINE
LOST	MINK
LOSE	MONK
LOBE	MOCK
LOVE	ROCK

Quiz 76 : Bible Workers and Materials

1. Dyer 2. Clay
3. Carpenter 4. Tanner
5. Nail 6. Goldsmith
7. Wood 8. Paint 9. Builder
10. Tailor 11. Paper
12. Artist 13. Fisher
14. Writer 15. Potter
16. Boat 17. (Across) Plough;
(Down) Pen 18. Baker
19. (Across) Axe; (Down)
Anvil 20. Mason 21. Net
22. Brick 23. Iron 24. Silver
25. Stone

Quiz 77 : In an Eastern Kitchen

Quiz 78 : Columns of Truth

A.
1. Risen 2. Esau
3. Damascus 4. Eternal
5. Midday 6. Paul 7. Ten
8. Israel 9. Olives
10. Nimrod
Column: Redemption

B.
1. Hell 2. Yesterday
3. Passover 4. Oaks
5. Curry 6. Refiner
7. Iscariot 8. Thank 9. Evil
10. Servant
Column: Hypocrites

Quiz 79 : Time of Elijah and Elisha

A.
1. Nimshi 2. Joram
3. Hazael 4. Jehoram
5. Jehoshaphat 6. Jehu
7. Ben Hadad 8. Ahaziah

B.
1. Tishbe 2. Samaria
3. Carmel 4. Zarephath
5. Ramoth Gilead 6. Kerith
7. Damascus 8. Shunem

Quiz 80 : Criss-Cross

A. TRAVELLING ALONG

B. IN THE GARDEN

C. UP IN THE SKY

D. WHAT SHALL WE EAT AND DRINK?

Quiz 81 : Odd Man Out

A.
1. London not a Bible city
2. Potato not a Bible vegetable
3. Herod not an Old Testament king
4. Jude not written by Paul
5. Chestnut not a Bible tree
6. Orange not a Bible fruit
7. Caspian not a Bible sea
8. Danube not a Bible river
9. Joshua not a son of Adam
10. Platinum not a Bible mineral

B.
1. Elephant not a Bible animal
2. Gas not a Bible form of lighting
3. Joseph not a son of Noah
4. Zulu not a Bible tribe
5. Roosevelt not a missionary
6. Tulip not a Bible flower
7. Mauve not a Bible colour
8. April not a Bible month
9. Palace not a place of worship
10. Snowdon not a Bible mountain

Quiz 82 : Walking in the Light

1. Sin 2. Fellowship
3. (Across) Confess; (Down) Claim 4. Walk 5. Light
6. Have 7. Declare
8. Message 9. Live 10. Is
11. Lie 12. Truth 13. Heard
14. Sinned 15 (Across) Just; (Down) Jesus 16. The
17. Darkness 18. In 19. Son

Quiz 83 : 'S's All

1F 2D 3C 4E 5B 6J 7K
8A 9H 10G

Quiz 84 : Round We Go Again

A.
1. Ephraim 2. Image
3. Agent 4. Tabor 5. Orion
6. Only 7. Lystra

B.
1. Furnace 2. Cedar
3. Darts 4. Satan 5. Ankle
6. Leah 7. Ahijah

Quiz 85 : More Six-Letter Names

1. Hazael 2. Agabus
3. Dorcas 4. Ashdod
5. Gideon 6. Gilgal
7. Esther 8. Aquila 9. Elijah
10. Amalek 11. Hermon
12. Hannah 13. Siloam
14. Carpus 15. Ahiram
16. Persia 17. Festus
18. Baruch

Quiz 86 : Words of Jesus

A. Baal; worship B. Herod; Galilee C. Daniel; Saul
D. Yield; Heathen E. Star; Faster
Strip: Matthew 5:8

Quiz 87 : A Podful of 'P's

1C 2D 3I 4A 5H 6F 7G
8J 9K 10E

Quiz 88 : Going to Market

Quiz 89 : He Built a House

1. verse 3 2. verse 10 3. verse 9 4. verse 9 5. verse 3
6. verse 49 7. verse 20
8. verse 25 9. verse 36
10. verse 30

Quiz 90 : On the Sea in Ships

1. Joppa 2. Rudder
3. Merchant 4. Solomon
5. Cush 6. Tarshish 7. Dan
8. Egypt 9. Hiram
10. Malta 11. Patara
Centre column: Jehoshaphat

Quiz 91 : Bible Singing

1. Philippi 2. Praises
3. Spiritual 4. Noisy
5. Jubilant 6. Wedding
7. Thanksgiving
8. Deliverance

Quiz 92 : Lost Strings and Sounds of Music

1. Music 2. Harps 3. Lyre
4. Strings 5. Zither 6. Horn
7. Trumpet 8. Tambourine

Quiz 93 : Anglican Cathedrals

1G 2A 3T 4P 5I 6H 7L
8O 9J 10B 11C 12E 13R
14M 15N 16F 17S 18Q
19K 20D

Quiz 94 : Five Parts of the Day

1. Noon 2. Oak 3. Ken
4. End 5. (Across) Hoe;
(Down) Hen 6. Egg
7. Dawn 8. Arm 9. Mad
10. Ash 11. Night 12. Gog
13. (Across) Pig; (Down) Pit
14. Top 15. Pin 16. (Across)
Dam; (Down) Den
17. Morning 18. Inn
19. Evening

Quiz 95 : Missing Words

1. Hopping 2. Jumped
3. Walk 4. Leap 5. Run
6. Swim 7. Crawl 8. Follow
9. Fly 10. Fall 11. Ride
12. Flee

Quiz 96 : Elijah on Carmel

1. Spears 2. Sacrifice
3. Noon 4. Sleeping
5. Ahab 6. Asherah
7. Kishon 8. Sky 9. Fire
10. Stones 11. God
Centre column: Prophesying

Quiz 97 : Eight Nines

ACROSS 1. Persuaded
4. Thornbush 5. Snowdonia
DOWN 1. Petitions
2. Unionized 3. Delphinia
DIAGONALLY 1. Phoenicia
5. Sevenfold

*Quiz 98 : To Conclude a
Service*

A. Thirst; water B. Bread; out;
fog C. Choose; first
D. Jewel; burly
Strip: 1 Thessalonians 5:28

*Quiz 99 : Weights, Measures
and Coins*

1. Ark 2. Beka 3. Cab
4. Drachmas 5. Ephah
6. Feet 7. Gerahs 8. Hin
9. Inches 10. Jars 11. Keg
12. Log 13. Miles 14. Nile
15. Omer 16. Pim
17. Quarter 18. Ruth
19. Shekel 20. Talent

Quiz 100 : Crossword

ACROSS 1. Thresher 5. At
7. Israelite 11. Pie 12. Mob
13. Asa 14. Foe 16. Ian
18. Invisible 20. RE
21. Universe
DOWN 1. Trip 2. Rare